MACHINE GUNS

WORLD WAR 2 FACT FILES

Machine Guns

**PETER CHAMBERLAIN
AND TERRY GANDER**

Arco Publishing Company, Inc.
New York

Published by Arco Publishing Company, Inc.
219 Park Avenue South, New York, 10003

Copyright © 1974 Peter Chamberlain and Terry Gander
ISBN 0-668-03506-4

Printed in Great Britain

Introduction

Of all the hideous 'engines of war' produced in the twentieth century, none has exacted a more dreadful toll of human life than the machine gun. Invented during the latter half of the nineteenth century, it reached the peak of its destructive powers during World War I, when the military and political course of the world for the next three decades was dictated by the dominance of the machine gun over the battlefield. During World War 2 the machine gun never did regain the dominance it held in World War 1. This was due mainly to the more mobile and fluid conditions imposed by mechanical warfare, but whenever a front became stabilized, the machine gun often emerged to dominate the tactical scene.

Many World War 1 guns were still in use during 1939-1945. This was due primarily to the machine gun's two mechanical attributes—reliability and durability. In 1939 the British and Commonwealth armies still used the Vickers gun, the Germans still had their MGO8 and the Italians their Fiat 14. The Americans retained their Browning M1917 and many European armies continued to use the elderly Schwarzlose. It was the Russians who kept on the oldest design in the shape of the M1910 Maxim—a direct copy of the original Maxim model. All these older designs depended on the gun's recoil to operate, but some guns developed during and just after World War 1 came to rely on a gas-operated mechanism that functioned by tapping-off gases produced when a cartridge is fired. These guns could be lighter and thus led to a new form of weapon, the light machine gun (or LMG). It had its origins during the First World War in the shape of the Lewis and Chauchat guns, both of which gave the infantry squad increased fire-power rather than having to depend on the heavy machine gun usually controlled at company or battalion level. The increased fire-power generated greatly influenced infantry tactics between the wars. Typical of the new light machine guns produced between 1920-1939 were the Czech ZB26 and 30 (and from them the British Bren) and the French Chatellerault guns.

But by 1939 another family of guns had emerged. One of the clauses of the Versailles Treaty prevented Germany from developing sustained-fire weapons, which in 1919 meant water-cooled machine guns. The Germans circumvented this clause by developing in Switzerland an air-cooled machine gun with changeable barrels—a gun that was to become the MG34 via the interim Solothurn M29 and 30. The MG34 was able to combine the sustained fire-rate of the heavy machine gun with the relatively low weight of the light machine gun, and thus became the first member of a new family known as general purpose machine guns. These could be carried into action by one man when mounted on a bipod, or they could be mounted on a heavy tripod for continuous fire. The MG34 was intended to be replaced by the advanced MG42 but such was the demand for machine guns by the German forces that the two were used side-by-side. This German demand for machine guns was so great that large numbers of captured guns were pressed into service by them, and nearly every type of Western and Russian gun mentioned in the text was at one time or another in German service. Where possible the German designation for such guns has been given, but the prefixes le. (leichte—light) and s. (schwere—heavy) were not often used in practice.

Of all the combatant nations, the USA produced the highest total number of machine guns, and also some of the best designs. For example. the superlative Browning guns remain in service to this day. By general opinion the Italian designs were the worst for they were generally over-complicated and unreliable. Japanese guns were sound and workmanlike, but Japanese industrial capacity was never able to supply the needs of the Army. In the UK light machine guns were dominated by the Czech-derived Bren in the same way that the Vickers gun dominated the heavier end of the scale. But, in 1940, the UK was desperate for machine arms and bought large numbers of obsolete guns from the USA—it was these old weapons that formed much of the Home Defences in those desperate days. The Russian machine guns were characterized by one factor—weight. The M1910 Maxim as well as being the oldest design in use was also the heaviest and had to be dragged around on a miniature artillery carriage. Of their light guns, the DP series was very successful, and like most Russian guns it was reliable and robust.

In this book are guns that contain some of the most ingenious mechanisms ever devised by the mind of man. It is one of the tragedies of the twentieth century that the inventiveness lavished on the machine gun resulted in a higher death toll than has ever been produced by any single type of weapon.

AUSTRIA

Schwarzlose Machine Guns

The first Schwarzlose machine guns were produced in 1905, by Steyr in Austria. Unique in being the only machine gun employing the retarded blow-back system the gun was very heavy and solid and due to the blow-back mechanism a short barrel fitted with a prominent flash hider was used. In fact it was so heavy that the parts never seemed to wear out and in 1939 there were large numbers still in service all over Europe. Early models had to use oiled cartridges but this feature was later designed out, and there were many variations on the theme. The main models were the 07 and the 08, but these were later brought up to the same standard as the 1912 model, the 12. Listed below are the main users along with the eventual German designations where appropriate. The list is correct for 1939.

Austria: 8 mm   07/12   *sMG 7/12(oe)*
Jugoslavia: 7.9 mm   Mitralez 7.9 mm
  M07/12S   *sMG 247(j)*
Bulgaria: 8 mm
Holland: 7.9 mm
  Mitrailleur M08   *sMG 241(h)*
  Mitrailleur M08/13   *sMG 242(h)*
  Mitrailleur M08/15   *sMG 244(h)*
Rumania: 6.5 mm   07/12
Hungary: 8 mm   07/12 (7/31)
Italy: 8 mm   07/12   *sMG 261(i)*
Greece: 6.5 mm   M12   *sMG 202(g)*

DATA (07/12)

CALIBRE	8 mm	0.315 in
LENGTH	1066 mm	42 in
BARREL LENGTH	526 mm	20.75 in
WEIGHT OF GUN	19.9 kg	44 lb
WEIGHT OF TRIPOD	19.8 kg	43.75 lb
M.V.	620 m/s	2050 ft/sec
RATE OF FIRE	400 rpm	
TYPE OF FEED	250 round fabric belt	

1

1. *German troops using a Schwarzlose as an AA gun on the Russian Front*   2. *Schwarzlose 07/12*   3. *Dutch 7.9 mm Mitrailleur M08*   4. *Jugoslavian Mitralez 7.9 mm M07/12S*

2   3   4

5

5. Schwarzlose 07/12 on tripod intended for use in prone position 6. Dutch Hussars using their Schwarzlose machine guns on exercise before the 1940 invasion

6

CZECHOSLOVAKIA

ZB vz/26

The Czech firm of Ceskoslovenska Zbrojovka at Brno was formed soon after WW1 to market the Praga Model 24, a belt-fed light machine gun designed by Vaclav Holek. At the same time a magazine-fed model was introduced which became known as the ZB vz/26, although the Czechs sometime refer to it as the VZ26. This gun introduced in 1926 was a well-designed gas-operated gun which soon proved very popular and was exported all over the world. Many were ordered by the Czech Army and these were eventually taken over by the Germans in 1938. The ZB vz/26 was a very popular gun and was well made. Many overseas states took up licences for manufacture and the gun design eventually led to the British Bren Gun. The ZB vz/27 was essentially similar to the ZB vz/26 except for minor details. Listed below are the main user states of the ZB vz/26 along with the German designations where appropriate.

China: 7.92 mm   Type 26
Czechoslovakia: 7.92 mm   Kulomet vz/26   *MG26(t)*
Lithuania: 7.9 mm   *7.9 mm leMG 146/2(r)*
Jugoslavia: 7.92 mm   Puska-Mitralez 7.9 mm M26 'Brunn'   *leMG146/1(j)*
Rumania: 7.9 mm
Russia: 7.92 mm   Rutschnoj pulemet obr. 1926   *leMG146/2(r)*
Spain: 7.92 mm   FAO
Sweden: 6.5 mm   Model 39
Turkey: 7.92 mm
Japan: 7.7 mm   97 Shiki Sensha Kikanju

DATA
CALIBRE   7.92 mm   0.312 in
LENGTH   1161 mm   45.75 in
BARREL LENGTH   672 mm   23.7 in.
WEIGHT   9.6 kg   21.3 lb
M.V.   762 m/s   2500 ft/sec
RATE OF FIRE   500-550 rpm
TYPE OF FEED   20 or 30 round box magazine

1. A Type 26 in service with the Chinese in the ruins of Changteh, March 1944

1

3

4

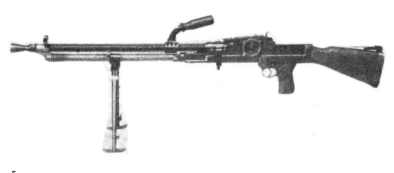

5

2, 3, 5. *ZB 26*   4. *Loading the ZB 26*
6. *MG 26(t)*   7. *Russian soldier
demonstrating a captured MG 26(t)*

6

7

ZB vz/30

The ZB vz/30 was a direct descendant of the ZB vz/26 and was almost identical to it—the only differences were minor and not easily seen. This model led, via the interim ZB vz/33, to the British Bren Gun and was thus the forerunner of a long line. Again, like its predecessor, it was exported all over the world and is still in service in some places in 1974. A list of the main users follows together with the eventual German designations where applicable.

ZB 30

Czechoslovakia: 7.92 mm   Kulomet vz/30   *MG30(t)*
Jugoslavia (30J): 7.92 mm   Puska-Mitralez 7.9 mm M.37 (Brünn)   *le MG148(j)*
Iran: 7.92 mm and 0.30 in
Spain: 7.92 mm   FAO
Rumania: 7.92 mm
Turkey: 7.92 mm

DATA
CALIBRE   7.92 mm   0.312 in
LENGTH   1161 mm   45.75 in
BARREL LENGTH   635 mm   25 in
WEIGHT   10.03 kg   22.125 lb
M.V.   745 m/s   2450 ft/sec
RATE OF FIRE   500-550 rpm
TYPE OF FEED   30 round box magazine

ZB vz/53

First produced in 1937, this model was known to the Czech Army as the Kulomet vz/37 and when the Germans took it over they called it the 7.92 mm MG 37(t) and used it as a standard issue gun. Although it was intended as a general purpose machine gun the British obtained a production licence and made it as a tank machine gun as the Gun, Machine, Besa. The Czechs also used the ZB vz/53 as a tank gun and as a tripod-mounted weapon, as did the Jugoslavs who used it as the Mitralez M40. When any of these were captured they were impressed as the 7.9 mm sMG 246 (j). One unusual feature of the ZB vz/53 was that it had two rates of fire that could be selected. It was a very reliable gun and was renowned for accuracy. Another unusual feature in such a heavy gun was that there was provision for a quick-change barrel.

DATA

CALIBRE 7.92 mm 0.312 in
LENGTH 1104 mm 43.5 in
BARREL LENGTH 671 mm 26.7 in
WEIGHT 18.6 kg 41 lb
M.V. 792 m/s 2600 ft/sec
RATE OF FIRE 500 or 700 rpm
TYPE OF FEED 100 or 200 metal link belt

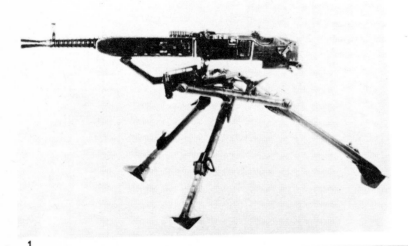

1

2

3

4

1, 2, 4. ZB 53   3. MG 37(t) in action with German Mountain troops   5. ZB 53 in service with the Chinese on the Yellow river, January 1944

5

ZB vz/60

MG M38(t) Kal. 15 mm in action

The ZB vz/60 appeared in 1938 and soon became one of the Czech armament industry's best sellers. In a very short time it was exported to Iran and Jugoslavia, and the British BSA organisation took out a licence to manufacture the type. In 1938 Czechoslovakia was taken over by the Germans and the gun continued in production for the German Luftwaffe and Navy. The ZB vz/60 was an enlarged version of the ZB vz/53 in 15 mm calibre and was intended both as a vehicle gun or an anti-aircraft weapon. The Germans used it mainly as an anti-aircraft gun as the MG M38(t)Kal. 15 mm. Jugoslavia used the gun as a heavy machine gun mounted on a special steel-wheeled carriage or on an anti-aircraft tripod. They called their version the Mitralez 15 mm M38, and when the Germans took over Jugoslavia in 1941 these guns became the 15 mm FlaMG 490(j). Any guns that were manufactured for the Germans in Czechoslovakia after 1938 were known as the 15 mm FlaMG 39 but it was identical to the ZB vz/60. Despite the widespread issue of this gun to the German forces it was not used a great deal, and it was mainly confined to static defences.

DATA

CALIBRE   15 mm   0.59 in
LENGTH   2050 mm   80.7 in
BARREL LENGTH   1463 mm   57.6 in
WEIGHT   55 kg   121.3 lb
M.V.   819 m/s   2685 ft/sec
RATE OF FIRE   420 rpm
TYPE OF FEED   40 round belt

DENMARK

The Madsen Machine Guns

The first Madsen light machine gun was produced in 1904 and thereafter it remained in production until the late '50s. During those years it was produced in a bewildering array of models and calibres, and it was sold all over the globe. Exactly why this gun was so widely used is not at first clear as it was expensive to make and buy, but it was very reliable despite the rather complex mechanism. It was produced for a variety of roles and was fitted into AFVs and aircraft, as well as being used in AA roles. The guns sold to the UK were used mainly as trial weapons but many were used by the Home Guard, while the German guns were those turned out by the production line during the Occupation. Many of the Dutch guns were captured by the Japanese in the East Indies, and used by them. Listed below are the main users involved in WW2 along with the usual German designation where applicable.

Bulgaria: 8 mm   M1915, 1924, 1927
China: 7.92 mm   M1916, 1930, 1937
Denmark: 8 mm   Rekytgevaer M1903/24
8 mm leMG 158(d)   Rekytgevaer M1924
8 mm leMG 159(d)   Rekytgevaer
Madsen   *8 mm sMG 258(d)*
Estonia: 0.303 in   M1925, 1937
Finland: 7.62 mm   M1910, 1920, 1921, 1923
France: 8 mm   M1915, 1919, 1922, 1924
8 mm leMG 157(f)
Germany: 7.92 mm   M1941, 1942
7.92 mm MG (Madsen)
Holland: 6.5 mm   M1919, 1923, 1926, 1927, 1934, 1938, 1939
Hungary: 7.92 mm   M1925, 1943
Italy: 6.5 mm   M1908, 1910, 1925, 1930
Jugoslavia: 7.92 mm
Lithuania: 7.92 mm   M1923
Norway: 6.5 mm   Maskingevaer m/14(mg m/14)   *6.5 mm leMG 102(n)*
Maskingevaer m/22(mg m/22) *6.5 mm leMG 103(n)*
UK: 0.303 in   M1915, 1919, 1929, 1931 1939

DATA (0.303 in)
CALIBRE   7.7 mm   0.303 in
LENGTH   1143 mm   45 in
BARREL LENGTH   584 mm   23 in
WEIGHT   9.07 kg   20 lb
M.V.   715 m/s   2350 ft/sec
RATE OF FIRE   450 rpm
TYPE OF FEED   20, 25, 30 or 40 round box magazine

1

2

4

3

1. Danish Madsen Rekytgevaer M1903/24
2. 8 mm Rekytgevaer Madsen   3. Madsen in Norwegian service   4. French M1922 Madsen, the 8 mm Fusilmitrailleur 'Madsen' Mle 1922

FINLAND

Automaattikivaari Lahti-Saloranta Malli 26

Usually referred to as the m/26 in Finland, this gun was designed by Aimo Lahti in 1926. It was a straightforward recoil-operated gun with a rather low rate of fire, and it remained in service with the Finns until the late '40s. It was used throughout the 1939-40 'Winter War' and was used during the Siege of Leningrad, but was little used elsewhere despite efforts to interest other nations in the years before WW2. The only nation that bought any was China, so the efficient and sturdy m/26 never gained the reputation it deserved. The Chinese guns were of 7.92 mm calibre.

DATA

CALIBRE	7.62 mm	0.30 in	M.V.	800 m/s	2625 ft/sec
LENGTH	1180 mm	46.5 in	RATE OF FIRE	500 rpm	
BARREL LENGTH	566 mm	22.3 in	TYPE OF FEED	20 round box magazine	
WEIGHT	8.5 kg	19 lb		75 round drum magazine	

FRANCE

Hotchkiss Light Machine Guns

The first true light machine gun was the Fusil Mitrailleur Hotchkiss Modèle 1909. The gun is often referred to as the 'Benet-Mercier', and it used the same gas-operated mechanism as the larger Hotchkiss guns. Feed was by the usual metal strip used by all Hotchkiss guns, but on the Mle 1909 it was inverted—a feature that often led to feed troubles. During WW1 the Mle 1909 was widely used and it was also adopted by the UK and USA. By WW2 the Mle 1909 had been phased out of service in France and the USA, but stocks were kept in the UK and were used as airfield defence weapons and for such roles as AA guns on Defensively Equipped Merchant Ships (DEMS). In 1939 and 1940 some of the British guns were used as front-line equipment, and in Greece some were handed over to the Greek Army.

In 1922 another Hotchkiss light gun was produced and another in 1926. Both could be fitted with a variety of feed mechanisms instead of the usual Hotchkiss strip, but they were not widely used. Some were exported to Greece, and some went to South America.

Listed below are the main users along with the eventual German designations. The Germans made use of both main models, mainly as fortress guns.

Mle 1909

UK/Greece: 0.303 in Gun, Machine, Hotchkiss, Marks 1 and 1* 7.7 mm *leMG 136(e)* 7.7 mm *leMG 136(g)*

Mle 1922/1926

France: 6.5 mm Fusil-mitraileur Hotchkiss Mle 1922 *6.5 leMG 105(f)*
8 mm Fusil-mitraileur Hotchkiss Mle 1922 *8 mm leMG 105(f)*

Greece: 6.5 mm Hotchkiss Model 1926 *6.5 mm leMG 104(g)*
7.9 mm Hotchkiss Model 1926 *7.9 mm leMG 152/1(g)*
Hotchkiss Model 1926 (heavy barrel) *7.9 mm leMG 152/2(g)*

DATA	Mle 1909	Mle 1926
LENGTH	1190 mm	1220 mm
BARREL LENGTH	600 mm	550 mm
WEIGHT	11.7 kg	9 kg
M.V.	740 m/s	745 m/s
RATE OF FIRE	500 rpm	500 rpm
TYPE OF FEED	30 round metal strip	25 round strip

1. Greek Hotchkiss mounted on Vickers tripod *2. Members of an OCTU carrying out training on a Hotchkiss, 1940*

1

2

3

4

5

6

7

Hotchkiss Medium Machine Guns

Belgium: 7.65 mm Mitrailleuse 'Hotchkiss' *7.65 mm sMG 220(b)*
China: Various
France: 8 mm Mitrailleuse Hotchkiss Mle 1914 *8 mm sMG 257(f)*
Japan: 6.5 mm Taisho 3 Nen Kikanju
Jugoslavia: 8 mm Mitralez 8 mm M14H *8 mm sMG 257(j)*
Norway: 6.5 mm Hotchkiss's 6,5 mm mitralose m/98 *6.5 mm sMG 201(n)* 7.9 mm Hotchkiss's 7,9 mm mitralose m/98t *7.9 mm sMG 240(n)*
Poland: 7.9 mm Karabin maszynowy Hotchkiss (14/25) *7.9 mm sMG 238(p)* 8 mm Karabin maszynowy Hotchkiss (14) *8 mm sMG 257(p)*
Rumania: 8 mm M1914

DATA (Mle 1914)
CALIBRE 8 mm 0.315 in
LENGTH 1270 mm 50 in
BARREL LENGTH 775 mm 30.5 in
WEIGHT OF GUN 23.6 kg 52 lb
M.V. 725 m/s 2400 ft/sec
RATE OF FIRE 400-600 rpm
TYPE OF FEED 24 or 30 round metal strips 249 'strip-belt'

The first Hotchkiss machine gun to see service was the Mle 1897, closely followed by the export model, the Mle 1898. They were followed by the Mle 1900 and the Mle 1914. They were all very similar gas-operated guns with heavy air-cooled barrels, and all had the two features that immediately identify the Hotchkiss medium machine guns—the five large cooling rings round the end of the barrel, and the metal strip feed. This feed system was one of the gun's less useful points as it limited the length of bursts, so the Mle 1914 featured a form of belt feed in which 3 round 'mini-strips' were joined up in 249 round lengths. The Hotchkiss guns were robust and serviceable weapons and were widely used in a variety of calibres. They were, however, heavy and cumbersome, so by 1939 most had been relegated to static defensive roles. Below is a list of the main user countries, and as the Germans found captured examples of these guns useful for coastal defence and fortress installations, the German designations are included.

2

1

1, 2. Hotchkiss Mle 1914   3. Mle 1914 on the Western Front, 1940

3

4. *A Mle 1914 in service with the Vichy French* **5.** *Twin-mounted Mle 1914s, April 1940*

13.2 mm. Mitrailleuse Hotchkiss d 13 mm 2 Mle 1930

DATA
CALIBRE 13.2 mm 0.519 in
LENGTH 2413 mm 95 in
BARREL LENGTH 1651 mm 65 in
WEIGHT 37.5 kg 87 lb
RATE OF FIRE 450 rpm
TYPE OF FEED 30 round box magazine
  15 or 20 round strips

Following on from the success of the 11 mm 'Modele de Ballon' of 1917, in 1930 the Hotchkiss firm produced an enlarged and modernized version as the Mitrailleuse Hotchkiss d 13 mm² Mle 1930. It resembled an enlarged Bren gun and embodied the Hotchkiss gas-operated mechanism together with an overhead 30 round curved box magazine. It was intended for a variety of roles and for each role a different mounting could be provided. Listed are the main types.

Anti-tank and Infantry use. Affût d'accompagnement à roues à une mitrailleuse 'Hotchkiss' de 13 mm² de cavalerie. This mounting resembled a small artillery mounting and ran on two spoked wheels. A small limber for ammunition and spares was part of this equipment.

Cavalry support. Affût-trépied leger de cavalrie à une mitrailleuse 'Hotchkiss' de 13 mm². Like the above mounting, this tripod was intended for cavalry support, but from fixed positions. It could be adapted for the AA role.

Anti-aircraft. Affut-trepied R₃ à deux Mitrailleuses Hotchkiss de 13 mm². This complex and heavy mounting could mount two 13.2 mm Hotchkiss guns for high-angle firing and a complex sighting device was fitted. A single-gun version was also used.

The 13.2 mm Hotchkiss was exported to Poland, Russia, Rumania, Jugoslavia, and Greece, but only in small numbers as it was an expensive and complex weapon. In 1940 the French guns were taken over by the Germans as the 13.2 mm MG 271(f) and many were emplaced in coastal defences. The Japanese produced a copy as the Type 93.

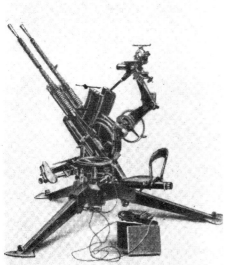

13.2 mm Mitrailleuse Hotchkiss d 13 mm 2 Mle 1930

Mitrailleuse St Etienne Mle 1907

The St. Etienne machine gun was a development of the Puteaux Mle 1905, which in its turn, was a state arsenal attempt to improve on the basic Hotchkiss design. By all accounts the St. Etienne gun, first built in the state arsenal in 1907, was not a great success. It underwent some radical modifications in 1915 and 1916 but these changes did little to improve a rather poor and unreliable design. After WW1 many were shipped out to the French colonies but some were embodied into the Maginot line defences. Others were sold to Greece, Jugoslavia and Rumania, but in 1939 and 1940 most of the St. Etienne guns came under German control. The Germans did give the gun a designation—the 8 mm sMG 256(f), (j) or (g)—but the St. Etienne seems to have been one captured gun they did not make use of.

1

DATA

CALIBRE	8 mm 0.315 in
LENGTH	1180 mm 46.5 in
BARREL LENGTH	710 mm 28 in
WEIGHT	25.4 kg 56.75 lb
M.V.	700 m/s 2300 ft/sec
RATE OF FIRE	400-600 rpm
TYPE OF FEED	24 or 30 round metal strips

1, 3. St. Etienne in action as AA gun, France 1940 2. Mitrailleuse 'St. Etienne' Mle 1907

2

3

Fusil-Mitrailleur Mle 1915—Chauchat

Sometimes referred to as the CSRG, the Chauchat machine gun was designed by a commission of designers in 1915. It soon earned the title of the most hated gun ever issued to soldiers as it was unreliable, poorly made, and difficult to use efficiently. The gun gave rise to a series of fraud and graft charges among the manufacturers, mainly due to the poor materials used in manufacture, but besides that, the gun operated on a long-recoil system that to put it mildly, was not efficient. Some small changes were made, but the gun never got over its first reception. By 1939 many of the large numbers made were used as reserve guns but others were in use in other armies (see list below). The Chauchat was one of the few captured weapons the Germans did not make use of, but in typical fashion they gave captured weapons a German designation and where appropriate this has been added to the list. Despite the abuse heaped on the Chauchat, it must be said that it has stood the test of time for some were encountered in the Vietnam conflict.

France: 8 mm Fusil-mitrailleur Mle 1915
 8 mm leMG 156(f)
Belgium: 7.65 mm Fusil-Mitailleur 15-27
 7.65 mm leMG 126(b)
Greece: 8 mm 7.8 mm 'Gladiator'
 8 mm leMG 156(g)
Jugoslavia: 7.9 mm Puska-Mitralez
 7.9 mm M15/26 *7.9 mm leMG 147(j)*
 8 mm Puska-Mitralez 8 mm M15
 8 mm leMG 156(j)
Rumania: 8 mm Model 1915

DATA

CALIBRE	8 mm 0.315 in
LENGTH	1143 mm 45 in
BARREL LENGTH	470 mm 18.5 in
WEIGHT	9.2 kg 20 lb
M.V.	700 m/s 2300 ft/sec
RATE OF FIRE	250-300 rpm
TYPE OF FEED	20 round curved magazine

Fusil Mitrailleur Mle 1915—Chauchat

Fusil-mitrailleur Darne Mle 1922

DATA
CALIBRE 6.5 or 8 mm 0.256 or 0.315 in
LENGTH 1120 mm 44.1 in
BARREL LENGTH 600 mm 23.625 in
WEIGHT 9.7 kg 21.4 lb
RATE OF FIRE 650 rpm
TYPE OF FEED 100 or 250 round belts

In many ways the Darne Mle 1922 was a remarkable machine gun. It was developed from the Darne Mle 1918, and heralded the manufacture and assembly methods that were to reach their peak with the German MG42. At a time when contemporary machine guns were being built and machined virtually as hand-made items, the Darne was designed for cheapness and ease of manufacture. It looked cheap and nasty but it was an efficient weapon that soon saw wide service as an aircraft gun, and the Darne was built in Spain and Czechoslovakia under licence. It was produced in France in both 6.5 and 8 mm and in Czechoslovakia in 7.92 mm. Some of the Czech guns ended up in Jugoslavia. Some of the Spanish guns were built as 7.5 mm aircraft guns. After 1940 the Germans used the Darne guns as the 6.5 mm or 8 mm leMG 106 (f)—mainly as coastal defence guns. Some were emplaced in turrets in the Channel Islands.

Darne Mle 1922

The Chatellerault Guns

DATA	Mle 1924/29	Mle 1931
CALIBRE	7.5 mm (0.295 in)	7.5 mm
LENGTH	1007 mm	1030 mm
BARREL LENGTH	500 mm	600 mm
WEIGHT	8.93 kg	11.8 kg
M.V.	820 m/s	850 m/s
RATE OF FIRE	450-600 rpm	750 rpm
TYPE OF FEED	25 round magazine	150 round drum magazine

The first of the light machine guns intended to replace the unsatisfactory Chauchat was introduced into French service in 1924. This was the Fusilmitrailleur Mle 1924, a light handy gun based on the Browning Automatic Rifle. It had the unusual feature of two triggers—the back one was for automatic fire and the front for single-shot. A new round was developed for this gun but neither it nor the gun was fully developed before entering service and there were several cases of exploding barrels which did little to boost confidence in the gun, and did little to boost possible exports. Further development work produced the modified Mle 1924/29 and this was the machine gun that most of the French Army went to war with in 1939. Identical in most respects to the Mle 1924 the Mle 1924/29 was the best of the French machine guns and served on for many years after the war, but in 1940 the Germans captured large numbers of them and used them in coastal defences. The Mle 1924/29 became the 7.5 mm leMG 116(f) and the few remaining Mle 1924 guns became the 7.5 mm leMG 115(f).

A further development of the Mle 1924/29 was the Mitrailleuse de 7.5 mm Mle 1931. This gun was designed for use in the Maginot line defences and as an extra could be installed in tanks. It had a peculiarly shaped butt and a distinctive 150 round drum magazine mounted on the left. After 1940 the Germans made great use of this gun, not only in coastal defences, but also mounted on a variety of makeshift mountings for AA use. The full German designation was 7.5 mm KpfwMG 331(f).

1. Fusil Mitrailleur Mle 1924/29   1

2

3

4

5

6

2. Searching a village, 1939 3. A 7.5 mm KpfwMG 311(f) emplaced for use as an AA gun. A make-shift butt has been added. 4. Mle 1924/29 5. Mitrailleuse de 7.5 mm Mle 1931 6. Two Mle 1931 guns being inspected, France 1939

GERMANY

Mashinengewehr 08

Belgium: 7.65 mm Mitrailleuse 'Maxim'
7.65 mm sMG 221 (b)
China: 7.92 mm Type 24
Jugoslavia: 7.92 mm Mitralez 7.9 mm
M8M *7.9 mm sMG 248(j)*
Lithuania: 7.92 mm *7.9 mm sMG 248(r)*
Poland: 7.92 mm Maxsim 08 *7.9 mm
sMG 248(r)*
Turkey: 7.92 mm

DATA

CALIBRE 7.92 mm 0.312 in
LENGTH 1175 mm 46.25 in
BARREL LENGTH 719 mm 28.3 in
WEIGHT COMPLETE WITH SPARES 62 kg
137 lb
WEIGHT OF SLEDGE MOUNT 83 lb
WEIGHT OF TRIPOD MOUNT 65.5 lb
M.V. 900 m/s 2925 ft/sec
RATE OF FIRE 300-450 rpm
TYPE OF FEED 250 round fabric belt

The sMG 08 was built by the Deutsche Waffen und Munitionsfabriken at Spandau, Berlin, and is thus often referred to as the 'Spandau'. During WW1 it took a fearsome toll of lives and in 1919 this gun was responsible for the inclusion of a clause in the Versailles Treaty prohibiting the development of water-cooled machine guns. A small number of sMG 08s were allowed to be retained by the German Army and Police and in 1939 many of them were still in service. In 1939 the process of re-equipping with the MG34 was far from complete and the MG08 was kept on. By 1942 it had been relegated to second-line duties such as training, airfield defence and coastal defences. The MG08 was a heavy, solid gun, and like all Maxim-type weapons was very reliable and just wouldn't wear out. It was mounted on either the heavy Schlitten 08 sledge mounting, or the later Dreifuss 16 tripod, and a few were mounted on captured British Bren Gun Carriers. Many were still in service in 1945, and the German guns were augmented by numbers of captured exported guns (see list below). Of these captured guns the Russian equipment came to the Germans via a tortuous path. Many of the 08 guns captured by the Germans in 1941 were originally German guns handed out to Lithuania and Poland in 1919. In 1939 the Russians took over Lithuania and part of Poland was annexed; any weapons taken over went into the Russian armouries ready to be captured in 1941 and 1942. Listed below are the main users along with the eventual German designation where appropriate.

1

2

3

1. MG08 emplaced as part of the 'Atlantic Wall', 1943 2. Belgian 7.65 mm Mitrailleuse 'Maxim' 3. Chinese Type 24 4. Jugoslav Mitralez 7.9 mm M8M 5. MG08 on AA mount

4

5

Mashinengewehr 08/15

The MG 08/15 started life in WW1 as an attempt to produce a lighter version of the MG 08 for use by assault troops. It retained the mechanism and water-cooling of the MG 08 but used a bipod, pistol grip and shoulder stock. It was still heavy for its role, but in 1939 it was still in service. By 1941 it had been relegated to second- and third-line duties and in 1945 was still in use. Many exported guns were taken over by the Germans and these are listed below. The Russian guns were originally handed over to Lithuania as reparations in 1919 and were seized by the Russians in 1939.

Belgium: 7.65 mm   Mitrailleuse 'Maxim' légère   *7.65 mm leMG 125(b)*

Jugoslavia: 7.9 mm   Leki-Mitralez 7.9 mm M8/15M   *7.9 mm leMG 145(j)*

Russia: 7.9 mm   Rutschnoj pulemet „Maksima" obr. 08/15   *7.9 mm leMG 145(r)*

DATA

CALIBRE   7.92 mm   0.312 in
LENGTH   1400 mm   57 in
BARREL LENGTH   719 mm   28.3 in
WEIGHT COMPLETE   18 kg   39 lb
M.V.   900 m/s   2925 ft/sec
RATE OF FIRE   450 rpm
TYPE OF FEED   50, 100 or 250 round fabric belt

1

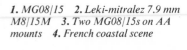

1. MG08/15   2. Leki-mitralez 7.9 mm M8/15M   3. Two MG08/15s on AA mounts   4. French coastal scene

2

3

4

Maschinengewehr Modell 13

This gun was an air-cooled rebuild of old WW1 Dreyse MG15 water-cooled machine guns. It entered service with the German Army in 1932 but by 1938 most of these guns, known as the MG13, were sold off to Portugal. Some, however, remained and were used in small numbers by various second-line units and others cropped up on the second-hand market.From this latter source some were obtained by Russia and others were used by various resistance forces.

DATA
CALIBRE   7.92 mm   0.312 in
LENGTH   1466 mm   57.75 in
BARREL LENGTH   717 mm   28.25 in
WEIGHT EMPTY   10.89 kg   24 lb

M.V.   823 m/s   2700 ft/sec
RATE OF FIRE   650 rpm
TYPE OF FEED   25 round box magazine
      75 round saddle drum

MG 13

Knorr-Bremse MG35

The MG35 started as a Swedish design—the 6.5 mm LH33. In 1935 the German brake firm of Knorr-Bremse bought the patents and produced a version in 7.92 mm as the MG35. This was offered to the German Army but they declined the offer; the only customers were the Waffen-SS who used it as a training gun and issued some to their 'Foreign Legions'. As a design it was somewhat unremarkable, but efforts were made to keep down cost. In 1940 some were sold to Finland but the number involved was never large and production ceased after 1940.

DATA

CALIBRE	7.92 mm 0.312 in		WEIGHT	10 kg 22 lb
LENGTH	1308 mm 51.5 in		M.V.	792 m/s 2600 ft/sec
BARREL LENGTH	691 mm 27.25 in.		RATE OF FIRE	490 rpm
			TYPE OF FEED	20 round box from left

MG35

Solothurn MG30

Although the Solothurn firm was situated in Switzerland it was financed and owned by the Rheinische Metallwaaren und Maschinenfabrik AG—later to be more familiarly known as Rheinmetall-Borsig, the German armament giant. They took over the Swiss company in order to carry out research into air-cooled machine guns to circumvent the terms of the Versailles Treaty that forbade the development of water-cooled machine guns. In 1929 the 'Solothurn designers' produced their Modell 29, a 7.92 mm weapon that incorporated many novel features. It had a quick-change barrel, an all-in-line mechanism, a high rate of fire and an unusual trigger mechanism. In the trigger, an arrangement was made that resembled 'The Man in the Moon'. Pressure on the top half produced single shot fire, while pressure on the lower portion produced automatic fire. The MG29 was slightly altered into the MG30 and offered to the Germany Army, but they turned it down; the gun was sold to Austria and Hungary who took about 5,000 between them. The MG30 was developed further by Rheinmetall and it became the starting point for the later MG15 and eventually the very successful MG34.

DATA

CALIBRE	7.92 mm 0.312 in		WEIGHT	7.7 kg 17 lb
LENGTH	1174 mm 46.25 in		M.V.	760 m/s 2500 ft/sec
BARREL LENGTH	596 mm 23.5 in		RATE OF FIRE	800 rpm
			TYPE OF FEED	25 round box magazine

Solothurn MG30

Maschinengewehr 15

The MG15 was one of the German machine guns that could trace their ancestry back to the Solothurn Modell 29 (q.v.) and this gun was further developed in Germany to produce an aircraft gun. The development work was carried out by Rheinmetall in 1932 and the Solothurn gun became the T6-200 (fixed) and T6-220 (flexible), but these designations were soon changed for both to become the MG15. As such it was widely used as an aircraft gun, but after WW2 had been in progress for a few years the demand for infantry machine guns was so great that some MG15 were converted to the ground role by the addition of a bipod and a short stock. It produced automatic fire only, and was a long and rather awkward weapon—not many were used. The 7.92 mm Type 98 was a licence-built version of the MG15 used in Japanese Army aircraft—the similar Type 1 was used by the Japanese Navy.

DATA
CALIBRE 7.92 mm 0.312 in
LENGTH 1334 mm 52.5 in
BARREL LENGTH 595 mm 23.5 in
WEIGHT 12.7 kg 28 lb
M.V. 755 m/s 2480 ft/sec
RATE OF FIRE 850 rpm
TYPE OF FEED 75 round saddle drum

1, 2. MG15   3. MG15 in use by Luftwaffe personnel defending an airfield used by Bf109s

2

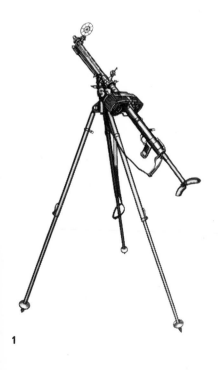

1

3

Maschinengewehr 34

Design of what was to become the German Army's most important machine gun began in 1934 at the Mauser plant at Obendorff. Starting point was the Solothurn MG29 and 30 and the resultant gun, the MG34, incorporated many of the design features of that weapon including the rapid barrel-change, in-line mechanism and trigger arrangement. But the new gun went a stage further and incorporated many new features that turned the MG34 away from being a light machine gun into the first general-purpose machine gun. In the light MG role a simple bipod was provided but an AA mount—the Dreifuss 34—could be used for the AA role. For use as a heavy MG a heavier mounting—the MG-Lafatte 34—was provided and this too could be converted to the AA role. Numerous other special mountings were available for use on AFVs (including ball mountings), vehicles and emplacements, and twin and triple mountings for AA use. The MG34 entered service in 1936 and remained in production and service until 1945. It was a good gun and was very popular, and the high rate of fire was very effective. It saw widespread use with all arms of the German services, and any that were captured were often turned against their former owners—usually by resistance forces. The MG34 did have one major drawback for the Germans and that was that it was too good—this quality had to be paid for by a high cost in materials and manufacture which took an excessive toll of manufacturing facilities. As a result the MG42 was developed, but not before the MG34s and MG34/41 had been offered as high fire-rate alternatives. These two automatic-only models did not enter service.

DATA

CALIBRE 7.92 mm 0.312 in.
LENGTH 1219 mm 48 in
BARREL LENGTH 627 mm 24.75 in
WEIGHT WITH BIPOD 11.5 kg 26.7 lb
M.V. 755 m/s 2480 ft/sec
RATE OF FIRE 800-900 rpm
TYPE OF FEED 50 round belt linked to
 form 250 rounds
 75 round saddle drum (from MG15)

Twin MG34s mounted on a Zwillingslafette 34 fitted to a Doppelwagen, 1940

MG34 — Poland 1939

DATA

CALIBRE 7.92 mm 0.312 in
LENGTH 1220 mm 48 in
BARREL LENGTH 533 mm 21 in
WEIGHT WITH BIPOD 11.5 kg 25.5 lb
M.V. 755 m/s 2480 ft/sec
RATE OF FIRE Up to 1500 rpm
TYPE OF FEED 50 round belt

Maschinengewehr 42

Of all the many and varied machine guns used during WW2 the German MG42 was the most outstanding. In many ways, both from a production and a design standpoint, it was a remarkable achievement and it had a profound effect on machine gun design which persists to this day. It started life as the MG39/41 and was another Mauser weapon, but this time its origins can be traced to a combination of MG34 developments and Polish ideas. Like the MG34 it was a general purpose weapon with a host of alternative mountings but there were numerous design differences, the most important of which to the front line was an increased rate of fire. The locking system was new but simple, and a simple and easy method of barrel changing was incorporated—this latter feature was very necessary due to the high rate of fire. But the biggest innovation came with the manufacturing methods employed. The gun was designed to incorporate a large number of stampings and spot welds to keep down costs, speed manufacture and enable construction to be carried out by unskilled labour. The use of critical materials was kept to a minimum. The MG42 first saw service in North Africa in 1942 and from then on it was one of the most feared of German weapons. Its high fire rate produced a sound like tearing linoleum, and this high fire rate tended to make the gun rather inaccurate on its bipod but the fire-power produced was prodigious and lethal. A late development, the MG45, had a different mechanism and an even higher rate of fire but it was only just entering service as the war ended.

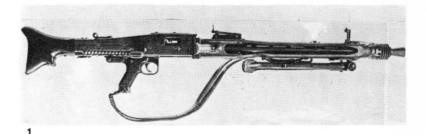

1

*1, 4, 5, 6, 7. MG42 2. MG42 im
Zwillingssockel 36 3. MG42 in action with
German mountain troops*

2

3

4

5

24

6

7

MG42

DATA
CALIBRE 15 mm   0.59 in
LENGTH 1916 mm   75.4 in
BARREL LENGTH   1254 mm   49.4 in
WEIGHT OF GUN   42 kg   92.6 lb
M.V.   790 m/s   2600 ft/sec
RATE OF FIRE   700 rpm
TYPE OF FEED   Linked 50 round belts

SdKfz 251/21 mounting three MG151/15

Maschinengewehr 151/15

The MG 151/15 was originally a Luftwaffe gun mounted in such aircraft as the Bf 109 and FW 190. As the war continued the fighter arm asked for, and got, heavier calibre guns than the 15 and 20 mm MG151 series so they were fitted to fewer and fewer aircraft. The Mauser assembly line then diverted their output to ground mountings to bolster AA defences. These applications were somewhat limited as the gun was electrically operated and installations had to have a 22-29 volt DC supply. The main use of the MG 151/15 was as a ground-to-ground weapon mounted in threes in the SdKfz 251/21, where the vehicles electrical supply could be used. These vehicles were first used during 1944. The MG 151 was built in both 15 and 20 mm calibres and both were used on the SdKfz 251/21. Each vehicle carried 3000 rounds in readiness. The data applies to the MG 151/15.

ITALY

Mitriaglice Fiat 14

During WW1 the Italians made use of large numbers of the Revelli modello 1914 machine gun in 6.5 mm calibre. These guns were mainly made by the Fiat organization and so the modello 1914 is often referred to as the 'Fiat-Revelli' or the Fiat 14. This gun had many odd features that gave it a reputation for unreliability. It had a retarded blow-back mechanism that needed an integral oiler to assist cartridge extraction. Above the gun body an external buffer rod was in a position to feed dust and dirt into the oiled interior and cause malfunctions. The feed system was unique and consisted of a magazine divided into ten compartments from which the rounds were fed into the gun from the right. In addition to the above features the 6.5 mm cartridge lacked performance, but in 1941 there were still large numbers of the modello 14 in service and the gun saw the war out. The Germans gave the gun the designation of 6.5 mm sMG 200(i), and the Jugoslavs used some as the Mitralez 6.5 mm (i)—here the German title was 6.5 mm sMG 200(j). What use the Germans made of these guns is not known. From 1935 the Italians modified the modello 14 into the modello 1914/35.

DATA
CALIBRE   6.5 mm   0.256 in
LENGTH   1181 mm   46.5 in
BARREL LENGTH   654 mm   25.75 in
WEIGHT OF GUN   16.9 kg   37.5 lb
WEIGHT OF TRIPOD   22.3 kg   49.5 lb
WEIGHT COMPLETE   39.2 kg   87 lb
M.V.   645 m/s   2110 ft/sec
RATE OF FIRE   450 rpm
TYPE OF FEED   50 round magazine

Mitriaglice Fiat 14

Mitriaglice Fiat 1914/35

From 1935 onwards large numbers of the old Fiat 14 machine guns were modernized to produce the modello 1914/35, and some guns were built from new as the modello 35. The main modification to the basic Revelli design was the change to the feed, which became a conventional belt feed type. The water jacket was removed and a heavy air-cooled barrel with a quick-change facility was added. At the same time the new 8 mm calibre was introduced and with it it was hoped that the need for the oiler would be removed. The same violent blow-back mechanism was retained, but it was hoped that the new round together with a fluted chamber would ease the extraction difficulties, but they remained and the oiler was re-introduced. Despite all the changes the modello 1914/35 was not a success as it had too many undesirable features, not least of which was the overheating of the barrel. By all accounts it was a worse gun than the old 1914 version, but as it was available in large numbers it saw the war through and was then promptly withdrawn from use. The Germans gave this gun the designation 8 mm sMG 255(i), but they do not appear to have made much use of them.

DATA
CALIBRE   8 mm   0.315 in
LENGTH   1263.5 mm   49.75 in
BARREL LENGTH   654 mm   25.75 in
WEIGHT OF GUN   17.9 kg   39.75 lb
WEIGHT OF TRIPOD   18.7 kg   41.5 lb
WEIGHT COMPLETE   36.6 kg   81.25 lb
M.V.   790 m/s   2600 ft/sec
RATE OF FIRE   500 rpm
TYPE OF FEED   300 round belt

Mitriaglice Fiat 1914/35

Fucile Mitriagliatori Breda modello 30

DATA
CALIBRE   6.5 mm   0.256 in
LENGTH   1232 mm   48.5 in
BARREL LENGTH   520 mm   20.5 in
WEIGHT   10.24 kg   22.75 lb

M.V.   629 m/s   2063 ft/sec
RATE OF FIRE   450-500 rpm
TYPE OF FEED   Fixed magazine taking 20
    round charger

The 6.5 mm Breda modello 30 was developed from the earlier modello 1924, 1928 and 1929, and became the standard Italian light machine gun of WW2. In many ways it was an unsatisfactory weapon, but it was all the Italians had during the African campaigns, and it served throughout the war. Perhaps the most trouble-some feature was the oil pump needed to assist extraction, since the operation of the lock was a modified blow-back. This oiler picked up dirt and clogged the mechanism, especially in dusty surroundings. Another weakness was the hinged magazine which was on the right of the gun. This was fixed to the body and hinged forward for loading from a cardboard or brass charger holding 20 rounds. If this magazine was

1, 2, 3. Breda modello 30   4. An Italian position near Agedabia, February 1941   5. A section of Italian infantry in action against the British near Marmacia in late 1941. A Breda modello 30 can be seen in the foreground

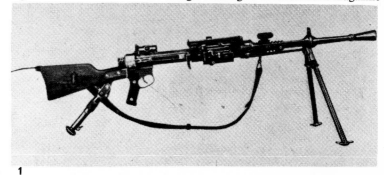

1

damaged or distorted the gun became useless. The barrel could be changed quickly but there was no handle provided to remove the hot barrel, and, as there was no carrying handle, carrying the modello 30 was awkward since the gun had many odd projections and corners. The Italian Navy used a similar gun, the modello 30/38, and a later variant was the modello 38 in 7.35 mm calibre (0.289 in). During the North African fighting, German troops sometimes used the modello 30 under the designation 6.5 mm leMG 099(i).

2

3

4

5

Mitriagliera Breda RM modello 31

DATA
CALIBRE   12.7 mm   0.50 in
WEIGHT   19.3 kg   42.5 lb
M.V.   793 m/s   2600 ft/sec
RATE OF FIRE   450-500 rpm
TYPE OF FEED   20 round overhead box
magazine

The Breda modello 1931 was produced as a tank machine gun in 13.2 mm calibre. It was a large heavy gun with an overhead box magazine holding 20 rounds which must have been a bit bulky in the close confines of an AFV interior, and the mechanism was conventionally gas-operated. Strangely enough there are very few facts available on this gun and virtually no data seems to exist. The modello 31 does not appear to have been very much used and its role would seem to have been very limited.

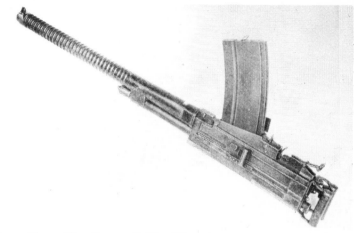

Breda RM modello 31 tank gun

Mitragliace Breda modello 37

DATA
CALIBRE   8 mm   0.315 in
LENGTH   1270 mm   50 in
BARREL LENGTH   740 mm   29.1 in
WEIGHT OF GUN   19.3 kg   42.8 lb
WEIGHT OF TRIPOD   18.7 kg   41.5 lb
WEIGHT COMPLETE   38 kg   84.3 lb
M.V.   790 m/s   2600 ft/sec
RATE OF FIRE   450 rpm
TYPE OF FEED   20 round strip

1, 2. Breda modello 37   3. Breda modello 38 tank gun

The Breda modello 37 became the 'standard' Italian heavy machine gun during WW2 and was the best of the Italian designs to see service. Using a fairly conventional gas-operated mechanism, the modello 37 was reliable and robust but it had the usual oil pump to aid extraction and the usual Italian MG feature, an unusual feed system. In the modello 37 rounds were fed into the gun from the side in 20 round flat trays. As the rounds were fired the empty cartridge cases were replaced in the tray, which then had to be emptied before reloading with fresh rounds. A special tripod mounting was designed for AA use. The Germans used small numbers of the modello 37 as the 8 mm sMG 259(i). A variant of the modello 37 was the Mitriaglice Breda calibro 8 modello 38 per carri armati. Produced in 1938 for tank use the modello 38 differed mainly in a conventional top-mounted curved box magazine. This was another gun used as the 8 mm Kpfw.MG 350(i), mainly mounted in Italian assault guns used by the Germans. The data applies to the modello 37.

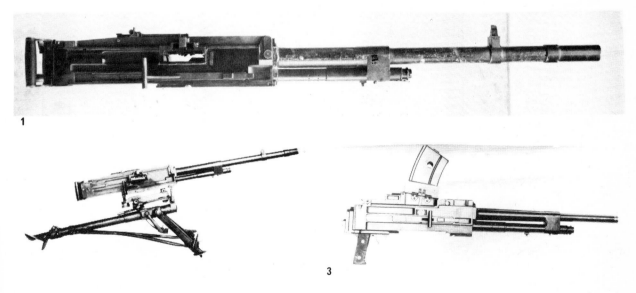

1

2

3

JAPAN

6.5 mm Heavy Machine Gun Type 3

During the Russo-Japanese War of 1904-1905, the Japanese used numbers of Hotchkiss Modèle 1900 heavy machine guns with telling effect. In 1914 the basic Hotchkiss design was slightly modified by altering the ejector mechanism and was produced in 6.5 mm calibre to become the Type 3, or Taisho 3 Nen Nikanju. This became the standard Japanese heavy machine gun for many years and outwardly resembled the usual Hotchkiss gun in many ways. The tripod mount had a typically Japanese modification in that it had fittings on the bases of the tripod legs to take poles or pipes which could be inserted enabling the gun to be carried short distances and brought in and out of action very quickly. The barrel had extra fins and an oiling mechanism to coat cartridges as they were fed from the usual Hotchkiss strip had to be incorporated. There were still many Type 3 machine guns in use in 1941 as the gun incorporated all the strength and reliability of the basic Hotchkiss design, but the lower-powered 6.5 mm cartridge had a poor performance at long ranges which led to its eventual planned replacement by the 7.7 mm Type 92.

DATA
CALIBRE   6.5 mm   0.256 in
LENGTH   1370 mm   45.5 in
BARREL LENGTH   745 mm   29.2 in
WEIGHT OF GUN   28.1 kg   62 lb
WEIGHT WITH TRIPOD   55.3 kg   122 lb
M.V.   742 m/s   2434 ft/sec
RATE OF FIRE   400-500 rpm
TYPE OF FEED   30 round metal strips

6.5 mm Heavy machine gun Type 3

6.5 mm Light Machine Gun Type 11

The Type 11 light machine gun entered service in 1922 and its design, based on the Hotchkiss principles, was unusual in many ways. It was designed by General Kijiro Nambu and was known as the Taisho 11 Nen Kikanju. As such it was the standard infantry light machine gun in 1941 and served throughout the war even though later guns were produced to replace it. Known to Western armies as the 'Nambu', the Type 11 had an unusual feed mechanism consisting of a hopper intended to take a stack of the standard rifle ammunition clips as used by the Japanese infantry squad. The idea was a good one but in practice the rather complicated mechanism gave constant trouble that could only be cured by using a special lower power cartridge, which rather negated the principle. However, the Type 11 was very widely used and its unusually shaped butt can be seen in many photographs of the Japanese Army in action. It was capable of automatic fire only and each round had to be oiled as it was fed. After the war, the Type 11 was widely used in China and was encountered in Vietnam.

DATA

CALIBRE 6.5 mm 0.256 in
LENGTH 1105 mm 43.5 in
BARREL LENGTH 482.6 mm 19 in
WEIGHT COMPLETE 10.1 kg 22.5 lb

M.V. 700 m/s 2300 ft/sec
RATE OF FIRE 500 rpm
TYPE OF FEED 30 round hopper taking five round clips

1. A Type 11 in action, China 1942
2. Type 11 with added padding under the barrel to assist carrying 3. Japanese troops in action in the Yenegyaung oilfields, Burma
4. 6.5 mm Light machine gun Type 11

1

2

3

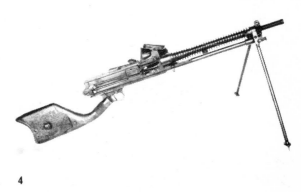

4

6.5 mm Tank Machine Gun Type 91

The Type 91 tank machine gun was a variant of the Type 11 designed for use in armoured vehicles. It entered service in 1931 as the 91 Shiki Kikanju, and was very similar mechanically to the Type 11. It did have a larger ammunition hopper holding 50 rounds, which must have been awkward to use in the close confines of a tank, and a telescopic sight was provided. Some were used as infantry weapons after the addition of a bipod, but the telescopic sight was retained.

DATA
CALIBRE   6.5 mm   0.256 in
LENGTH   838 mm   33 in
BARREL LENGTH   488 mm   19.2 in
WEIGHT   10.1 kg   22.4 lb
M.V.   700 m/s   2300 ft/sec
RATE OF FIRE   500 rpm
TYPE OF FEED   50 round hopper

6.5 mm Tank Machine Gun Type 91

6.5 mm Light Machine Gun Type 96

The Type 96 was intended as the eventual replacement for the Type 11 but Japanese war production never did catch up with the demand for machine guns so the Type 11 and 96 soldiered on side-by-side throughout the war. The Type 96 was a combination of principles copied from Hotchkiss and Czech ZB 26 designs which entered service in 1936 as the 96 Shiki Kikanju. It dispensed with the hopper feed of the Type 11 and replaced it with an overhead box magazine, but the dirt-catching oil dispenser had to be retained, even though the reduced power Meiji 30 cartridge was the specified round. A quick-change barrel was fitted, and the gun could use either drum or telescopic sights. One very unusual feature of the Type 96 was that it could be fitted with the Model 30 bayonet, making it almost unique among machine guns.

DATA
CALIBRE   6.5 mm   0.256 in
LENGTH   1054 mm   41.5 in
BARREL LENGTH   552 mm   21.65 in
WEIGHT   9.07 kg   20 lb
M.V.   730 m/s   c.2400 ft/sec
RATE OF FIRE   550 rpm
TYPE OF FEED   30 round box magazine

1

1. Type 96 showing magazine charging device
2. 6.5 mm Light Machine Gun Type 96
3. Type 96 with optional Type 99 portable armour shield and telescopic sight

2

3

7.7 mm Heavy Machine Gun Type 92

DATA (Type 92)
CALIBRE   7.7 mm   0.303 in
LENGTH   1156 mm   45.5 in
BARREL LENGTH   749 mm   29.5 in
WEIGHT WITH TRIPOD   55.3 kg   122 lb
M.V.   732 m/s   2400 ft/sec
RATE OF FIRE   450-500 rpm
TYPE OF FEED   30 round metal strips

The limitations of the small 6.5 mm cartridge were recognized by Japanese ammunition designers who produced in the early '30s a more powerful 7.7 mm round. New guns were produced to fire the new round, one of the first of which was the Type 92 heavy machine gun, which was produced in 1932 as the 92 Shiki Kikanju. In almost every respect, apart from the enlarged calibre, the new gun was the same as the Type 3, and it became the standard Japanese heavy machine gun. Strangely, no attempt was made to design out the oil dispenser or the metal strip feed, both of which continued to be bad design features of this gun, but even so the Type 92 served throughout the war. A lighter version was produced in 1941 with a shorter barrel—this was the Type 1. The Type 92 was nicknamed 'Woodpecker' by the Allies on account of its unmistakable sound when fired.

1

2

3

4

1. Type 92 on AA mount   2. 7.7 mm Heavy Machine Gun Type 92   3. Type 92 with carrying handles fitted

4, 5. Type 92 in action in Malaya

5

7.7 mm Tank Machine Gun Type 97

The Type 97 tank machine gun replaced the unsatisfactory Type 91 in service as the standard tank-mounted machine gun. It was a direct copy of the Czech ZB 26 machine gun altered to take the Japanese semi-rimless Shiki 92 round, and it entered service in 1937 as the 97 Shiki Sensha Kikanju. A large telescopic sight was fitted for tank use, and like most tank machine guns a bipod could be fitted for infantry use. The main drawback to the Type 97 was the retention of the curved box magazine which severely hampered its use inside a tank and efforts were made to produce belt-fed machine guns none of which were used in action.,

DATA
CALIBRE   7.7 mm   0.303 in
LENGTH WITHOUT STOCK   864 mm   34in
BARREL LENGTH   711 mm   28 in
WEIGHT   10.8 kg   24.5 lb
M.V.   732 m/s   2400 ft/sec
RATE OF FIRE   500 rpm
TYPE OF FEED   30 round box magazine

7.7 mm Tank Machine Gun Type 97

Type 97 with bipod fitted for infantry use

7.7 mm Machine Gun Type 99

The Type 99 machine gun was the best of all the Japanese machine guns to see service, and was issued in 1939 as the 99 Shiki Kikanju. It was a development of the earlier 6.5 mm Type 96 and the two guns were similar in many ways. The Type 99 used the Shiki 99 rimless round which did not need oiling and thus the dispenser mechanism could be omitted. An extra monopod leg was added under the heel of the butt which was adjustable and intended for extra firing stability at long ranges. Apart from the above changes the Types 96 and 99 were identical and even the unusual bayonet fitting was carried over. The Type 99 was never produced in sufficient quantities to meet demand, but there was a special paratroop version which could be easily stripped into sub-assemblies. After the war the Chinese converted some of these guns to take 7.92 mm ammunition, and both these and 7.7 mm versions were encountered in Vietnam.

DATA
CALIBRE   7.7 mm   0.303 in
LENGTH   1190 mm   46.75 in
BARREL LENGTH   545 mm   21.5 in

WEIGHT   10.4 kg   23 lb
M.V.   715 m/s   2350 ft/sec
RATE OF FIRE   850 rpm
TYPE OF FEED   30 round box magazine

7.7 mm Machine Gun Type 99

7.7 mm Machine Gun Type 92

The uncoordinated Japanese system of designating weapons led to the odd situation of two Type 92 machine gun versions in service at the same time. One was the 7.7 mm Hotchkiss-derived Type 92 and the other, the copy of the Lewis gun originally used by the Japanese Navy. Although the two guns were of the same 7.7 mm calibre they used different ammunition since the Lewis variant used a copy of the British 0.303 in round. The Lewis Type 92 was used in two main versions, one of which was intended mainly for aircraft use and dispensed with the large cooling jacket. With the cooling jacket the gun was used mainly for AA use and for base defence, but mounted on a tripod it was often used by both the Army and the Navy as a heavy machine gun. To complicate matters further there was a Lewis copy used by the Army air force as the 7.7 mm Type 89, which served alongside another Type 89 which was a 7.7 mm copy of the Vickers aircraft gun!

1. 7.7 mm Machine Gun Type 92 2. Type 92 aircraft gun

DATA

CALIBRE	7.7 mm 0.303 in	WEIGHT OF GUN	22 kg 49 lb
LENGTH	990 mm 39 in	M.V.	730 m/s 2400 ft/sec
BARREL LENGTH	610 mm 24 in	RATE OF FIRE	600 rpm
WEIGHT WITH TRIPOD	55.3 kg 122 lb	TYPE OF FEED	49 or 97 round drum magazine

1

2

13 mm Machine Gun Type 93

The 13 mm Type 93 was a copy of the 13.2 mm Mitrailleuse Hotchkiss d 13 mm
2. Mle 1930. The Japanese used this weapon mounted on all the various mountings
designed for it by the French. These included mobile and static AA mountings for
both single and dual gun combinations, and a variety of tripod and bipod mounts.
A model mounted on a wheeled carriage was known as the Kyusan Shiki Shasai
Jusan Miri Kikanju. The Japanese appear to have used these guns mainly as AA
weapons.

DATA

CALIBRE	13.2 mm	0.519 in
LENGTH	2413 mm	95 in
BARREL LENGTH	1651 mm	65 in

WEIGHT OF GUN	37.5 kg	87 lb
M.V. (BALL)	2,210 ft/sec	
RATE OF FIRE	450 rpm	
TYPE OF FEED	30 round box magazine	

13 mm Machine Gun Type 93

UK

The Bren Gun

DATA (Mark 1)
CALIBRE 7.7 mm 0.303 in
LENGTH 1155 mm 45.5 in
BARREL LENGTH 635 mm 25 in
WEIGHT 9.95 kg 22.12 lb
M.V. 744 m/s 2440 ft/sec
RATE OF FIRE 500 rpm
TYPE OF FEED 29 round overhead box
  magazine

The Bren Gun had its origins in the Czech ZB 26 and was developed via the ZB 27, 30, 33 and 34. By the time it was put into production at the RSAF Enfield Lock in 1937 it had been developed into what many armament experts believed was the finest light machine gun ever made, and as a measure of its success it is still in first line service with the British Army and many other armies in 1974. There were three main wartime marks with a number of sub-variants, but on all of them the basic gas-operated mechanism remained unchanged. The Mark 1 had an adjustable bipod, butt handle and a drum rearsight. Under wartime production conditions these 'luxuries' were removed and replaced by simpler and cheaper parts. The Marks 3 and 4 appeared in 1944 and were shorter, lighter and cheaper, and there were other post-war changes. Most Bren guns were at first produced at Enfield, but lines were started up in Canada, where versions were made in .303 in and 0.30 in and a special Mark 2 model was produced in 7.92 mm for China. Other lines were started in Australia and India, and the output from all these lines was directed to all Allied and Commonwealth armies. Many guns were sent into Occupied Europe to equip the various underground organizations. It was with these forces that the merits of the Bren showed to advantage, for it could be easily field-stripped and used with a minimum of training due mainly to its simple and rugged construction. In action it was reliable and accurate and for a light machine gun, not too heavy. Any Brens that fell into German hands were used by them as the 7.7 mm leMG 138(e). In British use the Bren was mounted on many different types of vehicle mounting and a variety of tripods was produced for just about every role a machine gun is called upon to play.

1. Bren Mk 1   2. Near Stein, Germany, January 1945. The Brens are the simplified Mk 2

1

2

3

4

3. A 'drill-book' picture of a Bren on its AA mount   4. A Bren Mk 1 on the little-used tripod developed for long-range firing, but convertible for AA use   5. Twin Brens on the Twin Motley mounting developed for vehicle and naval use. The magazines are the little-used high speed 200 round drums 6. Single Motley mount   7. Twin Brens on a Gallows mount   8. Twin Motley mount in use by Canadians, Calais, 1944

5

6

7

8

38

DATA (VB Mark 3)
CALIBRE 7.7 mm   0.303 in
LENGTH 1156 mm   45.5 in.
BARREL LENGTH 600 mm   23.6 in
WEIGHT 10.9 kg   24.4 lb
M.V. 745 m/s   2450 ft/sec
RATE OF FIRE 450-600 rpm
TYPE OF FEED 30 round box magazine

Vickers-Berthier Machine Guns

In 1925 Vickers obtained the manufacturing rights for the French Berthier light machine gun, and started to produce some for export, and for acceptance trials for the British Army. No orders came from the British as they ordered the Czech-derived Bren, but the Indian Army ordered large numbers and used them as their standard light machine guns. They bought numbers of the Mark 1 and 2, and then proceeded to manufacture their own guns at the arsenal at Ishapore as the Marks 3 and 3B. The Vickers-Berthier was a gas-operated gun very similar to the Bren in appearance and performance, and in 1933 it seemed very likely that the VB, as it was often known, would take over from the Lewis gun in British service, but it was not to be. Even in India, it was eventually replaced by the Bren—more for reasons of standardization rather than other causes for the VB proved to be a good reliable gun. In 1974 it is still in use in India. One of the export recipients was Lithuania, but when that state was taken over by Russia in 1939 the VB guns were used by them as the Rutschnoj pulemet 'Vickers-Berthier', mainly on second-line duties. Another VB design emerged as an aircraft gun intended for use in RAF two-seater aircraft of the Hart variety. This was the Vickers C.O. gun, or 'K' gun. It was soon taken over by events that meant the demise of the old open cockpit aircraft and the gun was gradually withdrawn from use with the RAF, even though it remained in use with the Fleet Air Arm until 1945. Many of the surplus guns found a useful role as vehicle guns in the Western Desert campaigns, where they were much favoured by such special forces as the LRDG and SAS. Others were used for airfield defence and AA guns. They were all .303 in guns weighing about 19.5 lb, with a rate of fire of 1,050 rpm. Feed was from an overhead drum containing 96 rounds.

1. Vickers G.O. or 'K' gun 2, 3. Vickers K guns in use as AA weapons in Malta
4. This SAS jeep in Italy is armed with five K guns

1

2

3

4

The Hefah Machine Gun

Very little is known about the Hefah machine gun. It was produced in small numbers for the Royal Navy after its development in 1940 and employed as an anti-aircraft gun on small coastal vessels and Defensively Equipped Merchant Ships (DEMS). It was a variation of the Lewis Gun, but the magazine was under the body and the mechanism was simplified. Official designation was Gun, Machine, Hefah V, 0.303 in Mark 1, but it was declared obsolete in November 1944, after being approved for service in May 1942. No data can be found for this gun.

The Hefah machine gun

Gun, Machine, Vickers, 0.303″, Mark 1

The Vickers Machine Gun entered service in 1912 and in 1974 it is still in world-wide use virtually unchanged from the first gun that left the Crayford production line. Vickers took the basic Maxim principle and inverted it to produce the mechanism that was to remain unchanged to this day. At the same time detail changes were made to construction methods and the result was one of the most rugged and dependable of all the heavy machine guns of WW2. The British Army and its Allies used the gun in all theatres of war, and it was also used by such states as Lithuania, Russia, Latvia, Holland and the USA. All the British Commonwealth countries used it. During its long life, there were some variations and changes, but these usually were of a minor nature that left the basis unchanged. For instance there were some guns produced with smooth rather than corrugated water jackets, and there were numerous variations in the muzzle recoil booster. A more fundamental change came with the introduction of the Mark 8z round which added a further 1000 yards to the 3600 yard range. This led to the fitting of an optional dial sight for indirect fire after 1942. During WW1 the USA adopted the Vickers gun in 0.30 in calibre as the M1915. In 1940 most of their remaining guns, 7,071 in all, were sold back to the UK where they were marked with red paint bands and used for home defence with the Home Guard. The USA did use some themselves in the 1941 defence of the Philippines. Elsewhere, the Russians used guns that came their way from the 1939 occupation of the Baltic States and others that remained from their Civil War of the '20s. The Germans pressed into service any captured guns as either the British 7.7 mm sMG 230(e) or the Dutch 7.7 mm sMG 231(h). Any captured Russian guns became the 7.7 mm sMG 230(r). Many of the 'German' guns were issued to the Volksturm in 1945.

DATA

CALIBRE	7.7 mm	0.303 in
LENGTH	1156 mm	45.5 in
BARREL LENGTH	721 mm	28.4 in
WEIGHT OF GUN WITH WATER	18 kg	40 lb
WEIGHT OF TRIPOD	22 kg	48.5 lb
WEIGHT COMPLETE	40 kg	88.5 lb
M.V.	744 m/s	2440 ft/sec
RATE OF FIRE	450-500 rpm	
TYPE OF FEED	250 round fabric belt	

1. The basic Vickers machine gun 2. Vickers guns being used as AA guns mounted on a special mounting intended for vehicles. Lyndhurst, September, 1940

1

2

3. *The ultimate Vickers gun in 1945 with dial sight and recoil booster* 4. *Indirect firing from a Vickers gun, France 1944* 5, 6. *Canadians using their Vickers guns on AA mounts* 7. *Vickers gun in North Africa*

3

4

5

6

7

.303″ Vickers Tank Machine Guns

The Marks of the Vickers Machine Gun developed for use in AFVs were the 4B, 6, 6* and 7. The 4B and 6 entered service in 1934 and the other two after 1938. They were all very similar adaptations of the basic Vickers design, with the main change being that a pistol grip and trigger was fitted in place of the usual spade grips. The water jacket was retained and connections provided on the Mark 6z for an internal header tank for coolant water. The mountings differed from mark to mark but they were all rather heavy, bulky and expensive. Most British AFVs carried a .303 in machine gun between the wars and the gun served mainly as a co-axial gun on cruiser and heavy tanks and as the main armament of many light tanks and armoured cars. They were eventually replaced by the 7.92 mm Besa guns.

DATA (Mark 7)
CALIBRE   7.7 mm   0.303 in
LENGTH   1100 mm   43.3 in
BARREL LENGTH   790 mm   31.1 in
WEIGHT   21.4 kg   47.2 lb
M.V.   744 m/s   2440 ft/sec
RATE OF FIRE   450-500 rpm
TYPE OF FEED   250 round fabric belt

1. Vickers Mk VI tank gun   2. Vickers Mk VII tank gun   3. Vickers tank gun dismounted for infantry use

.5″ Vickers Machine Guns

The first .5 in Vickers machine gun appeared in 1933 and was a scaled-up version of the .303 in Mark 1 with changes to take rimless ammunition and some other detail differences. There were three marks in use during WW2—the Marks 3, 4 and 5. The Mark 3 was a Navy gun in use on many ships as an AA weapon, often in quadruple mountings, and with a fire rate of 700 rpm. The Marks 4 and 5 were AFV guns with a lower fire rate which formed the main armament of many British light tanks and armoured cars at the beginning of the war. By 1944 only the Mark 3 Navy guns were still in use. There was one further variant, the Vickers Class D together with the D*. Used only in very small numbers during WW2 this was a land-based AA gun which fired a special high-velocity round.

1. Vickers .5 in Mk V tank machine gun 2. An ex-World War 1 Vickers Class D gun being inspected at South Shields, August 1940

DATA (Mark 5)

CALIBRE 12.7 mm 0.5 in	WEIGHT 29 kg 63.95 lb	
LENGTH 1190 mm 46.8 in	M.V. 793 m/s 2600 ft/sec	
BARREL LENGTH 790 mm 31.1 in	RATE OF FIRE 450 rpm	
	TYPE OF FEED 100 round belt	

7.92 mm Besa Tank Machine Guns

DATA (Mark 1)
CALIBRE 7.92 mm 0.312 in
LENGTH 1110 mm 43.7 in
BARREL LENGTH 736 mm 29 in
WEIGHT 21.15 kg 47 lb
M.V. 823 m/s 2700 ft/sec
RATE OF FIRE 450 or 700-750 rpm
TYPE OF FEED 225 round link or metal
and fabric belt

During the 1930s Czech designers had a large degree of influence on small-arms procurement in the UK, so it is not surprising that when a new tank machine gun was needed, Czech designs were considered., One such gun was the ZB vz/53, and it was this model that was chosen as the standard AFV gun for the war years. The original 7.92 mm calibre was retained as the conversion of the ZB 26 models into the Bren had bought about much extra development work to convert the design to take the British .303 in round. The Czech design was much modified to facilitate production and lower the cost, and eventually the gun ran to three basic wartime Marks. First came the Marks 1 and 2 in 1940, both with a two-rate selective fire feature. This was removed for the 1941 Mark 3, and there were several sub-variants. The Mark 3 also had several other design changes which made it some 20 per cent cheaper than the first model. The Besa guns were used in nearly all the British WW2 tanks and remained in use for many years after 1945. Since the Germans were in the habit of using captured Allied AFVs themselves, the Besa also got a German designation—in fact it was the 7.9 mm KpfwMG 341(e).

1

2

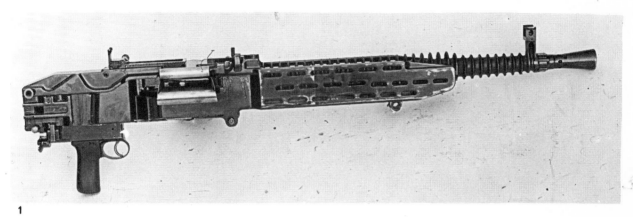

3

1. Besa Mk 1 2. Besa Mk 2 3. Besa Mk 3
4. A Besa pressed into AA use in 1940

4

15 mm Besa Tank Machine Guns

Yet another Czech design to be put into British production was the ZB vz/60, a large 15 mm design bought out in 1938. It was an enlarged version of the 7.92 mm gun designed for use only in AFVs, and production started at the BSA factory in 1939. First deliveries were made in 1940, and the gun was fitted to the Vickers Mark V1C Light Tank and was fitted to some experimental vehicles. Some were also fitted to armoured cars, especially the Humber Armoured Cars. Apart from the above vehicles, the 15 mm Besa was little used and production ceased after 3,218 had been made. The main drawback as far as the British were concerned was that the gun was too big and heavy for its purpose, but by the time the war had ended, such large guns were becoming commonplace on AFVs, so the 15 mm Besa can be said to have been ahead of its time. There was only one Mark, and design attempts to convert the gun to 20 mm came to nothing. Any vehicles the Germans captured with this weapon fitted were often turned against their former owners with the 15 mm KpfwMG 376(e).

DATA
CALIBRE   15 mm   0.59 in
LENGTH   2050 mm   80.7 in
BARREL LENGTH   1463 mm   57.6 in
WEIGHT   56.5 kg   125.5 lb
M.V.   819 m/s   2685 ft/sec
RATE OF FIRE   400-450 rpm
TYPE OF FEED   25 round link belt

15 mm Besa Mk 1

The Lewis Gun

It is difficult to place the Lewis gun under any national heading for it has been one of the truly international machine guns. It was invented by an American, Samuel Maclean, at the turn of the century, but it was developed and 'sold' by a Col. Lewis —another American. During WW1 it was not at first taken up by the USA but it was produced in Belgium and then the UK. When the USA entered the war, production started there as well, and large numbers were produced to equip the US forces. The Lewis gun was a gas-operated weapon with a mechanism that has stood the test of time, for it is still used in some modern designs. It was produced as an infantry weapon and also as an aircraft gun, both fixed and flexible. It was turned out in the USA, UK, Japan, Belgium and France between the wars and was exported to many states. In 1939 it was still in general use by many of the combatant nations, and in 1940 1,157 infantry guns and 38,040 aircraft guns were bought from the USA by the British to replace the guns lost in France in the campaign before Dunkirk. These guns were all 0.30 in guns and were known to the British as 'Savage-Lewis' guns. They were used alongside .303 in BSA-produced guns as low-level AA guns in single, double and quadruple mounts and in the Battle of Britain accounted for 20 per cent of all aircraft shot down around London. Many Lewis guns were used on merchant ships and also saw service with the Home Guard. Although there were many variations there were two basic versions—the ground version with an air-cooled jacket, butt and bipod, and the aircraft version with spade grips and a larger magazine, although there were often many changes to convert them for ground use. The USA still had many in use in 1941-42 in the Philippines, and the French guns, produced by the Société Armes Lewis-St. Denis were used by many small states. The Japanese copies saw extensive service in the Far East. Below is a list of the main users.

Estonia: 7.7 mm   Model 1914
France: 6.5 and 8 mm   Fusil-mitraileur 'Lewis' Mle 1924
Holland: 6.5 mm   Mitrailleur M20
6.5 mm leMG 100(h)
Japan: 7.7 mm   Type 89
7.7 mm   Type 92
Latvia: 7.7 mm
Portugal: 7.7 mm   M/917
Russia: 7.62 mm   Rutschnoj pulemet 'Lewis'   *7.62 mm leMG 122(r)*
UK: 0.303 in   *7.7 mm leMG 137(e)*
USA: 0.30 in

DATA (British Mk 1)
CALIBRE   7.7 mm   0.303 in
LENGTH   1250 mm   49.2 in
BARREL LENGTH   661 mm   26.04 in
WEIGHT   12.15 kg   27 lb
M.V.   744 m/s   2440 ft/sec
RATE OF FIRE   450 rpm
TYPE OF FEED   47 or 97 round overhead drum magazine

1

3

2

4

5

1. Lewis Mk 1   2, 4. Dutch Mitrailleur M20
3. 6, 7, 8. The Lewis was extensively used for
airfield and searchlight site defence
5. Fusil-mitrailleur 'Lewis' Mle 1924

6

9 to 13. American .30 in Savage-Lewis guns were used in their aircraft versions as AA guns by the Army, RAF and Home Guard

7

8

9

10

11

12

13

USA

Colt-Browning Model 1895

Russia: 7.62 mm Stankowiij pulemet 'Colt'
Belgium: 7.65 mm Mitrailleuse 'Colt'

DATA (Belgian)
CALIBRE   7.65 mm   0.301 in
LENGTH   1200 mm   47.25 in
BARREL LENGTH   720 mm   28.35 in
WEIGHT OF GUN   16.8 kg   37 lb
WEIGHT OF TRIPOD   29 kg   64 lb
WEIGHT COMPLETE   45.8 kg   101 lb
RATE OF FIRE   400-500 rpm
TYPE OF FEED   300 round belts

The Colt-Browning Model 1895 was the first practical machine gun design of John Browning to see production and service. It was a gas-operated gun with a swinging arm that came down into a vertical position when firing, underneath the barrel. This arm caused the gun to be known as the 'potato-digger', and prevented the gun being mounted close to the ground without first digging a small pit. The gun saw extensive service during WW1, but soon after was withdrawn from use as a first-line weapon. By 1939 very few were left and those still in use in Belgium and Russia were used mainly as training and second-line weapons. The Russian guns were relics of the Russian civil war of the '20s.

Colt-Browning 1895/1914

.30″ Marlin Machine Guns

DATA
CALIBRE   7.62 mm   0.30 in
LENGTH   1016 mm   40 in
BARREL LENGTH   711 mm   28 in
WEIGHT   10.1 kg   22.5 lb
M.V.   840 m/s   2750 ft/sec
RATE OF FIRE   500-700 rpm
TYPE OF FEED   120 or 250 round webbing belt

During WW1 Marlin-Rockwell took over production of the Colt-Browning Model 1895 and altered the basic design in order to expedite manufacture and at the same time get rid of the swinging arm under the gun. The result became known as the Marlin gun but it is sometimes referred to as the 'Marlin-Navy', although strictly speaking this should only refer to the guns converted from the original Model 1895. There were three main models, the M1916 and 1917 aircraft guns and the M1918 intended as a tank gun. By 1932 all these guns had passed from service with the US forces, and many were put into storage. In 1940 18,240 Marlin guns were supplied to the UK where they were used mainly as anti-aircraft guns on DEMS (defensively equipped merchant ships). Most of these guns were aircraft guns that had to be fitted with sights and fittings such as butts before they could be used.

1. Marlin Aircraft gun   2. Home-made mounting using two Marlin guns   3. Marlin gun converted for DEMS use

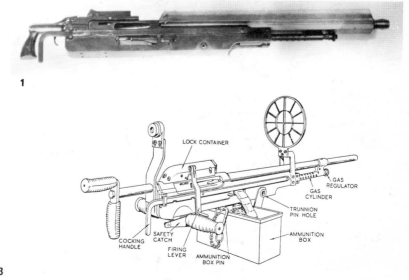

1

2

3

The Browning Automatic Rifle

The Browning Automatic Rifle, or BAR, occupies a peculiar place in WW2 weapon classification as to its main. users, the US forces, it was an automatic rifle; to the rest of the world it was a rather light light machine gun. It was a WW1 weapon designed to boost infantry fire power and during WW2 it was used as the US infantry squad support weapon. First developed in 1917, the BAR was first used in action in 1918 and ever since then it has been turned out in thousands in a wide variety of models. In 1974 it is still used by many countries, but it is no longer a first-line weapon with the US forces. There were three main models:

Model 1918. A hand-held gun—the first model.

Model 1918 A1. Provision was made for a bipod and a shoulder strap. A flash-hider was fitted.

Model 1919 A2. The WW2 variant, with a butt monopod fitted. This model had two rates of automatic fire, instead of selective fire, but this feature was sometimes removed.

In addition to the above the Belgian FN plant manufactured the BAR as the Model 30. It resembled the M1918A1 version with a few changes. Versions were produced for export in 7, 7.65 and 7.92 mm.

After Dunkirk the US government supplied 25,000 BARs to the UK. These guns were M1918 and 1918A1 versions and they were issued to the Home Guard and other home defence units. As far as is known, the British did not use any as first-line weapons. In Europe, Poland made use of the BAR, but after 1939 these were taken over by Russia and Germany.

Belgium: 7.65 mm   Fusil-Mitrailleur 1930
7.65 mm leMG 127(b)
China: 7.92 mm
Poland: 7.92 mm   Reczny karabin
maszynowy wz.28   *7.9 mm leMG 154(p)*
Russia: 7.92 mm   Rutschnoj pulemet
Browning obr. 1928
UK: 0.30 in.

DATA (M1918A2)
CALIBRE   7.62 mm   0.30 in
LENGTH   1214 mm   47.8 in
BARREL LENGTH   611 mm   24.07 in
WEIGHT   8.73 kg   19.4 lb
M.V.   808 m/s   2650 ft/sec
RATE OF FIRE   500-600 or 300-350 rpm
TYPE OF FEED   20 round box magazine

*1. BAR M1918   2. M1918A1
3, 4, 5. M1918A2*

1

2

3

4

5

6

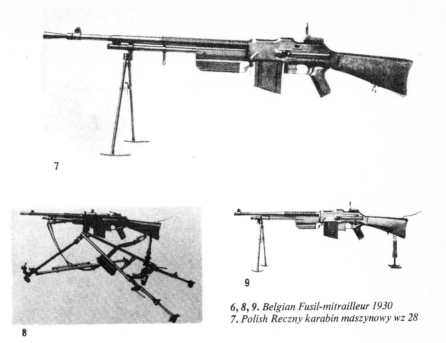

7

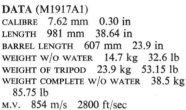

8

9

6, 8, 9. Belgian Fusil-mitrailleur 1930
7. Polish Reczny karabin maszynowy wz 28

US Machine Gun, Caliber .30″, M1917

DATA (M1917A1)
CALIBRE 7.62 mm 0.30 in
LENGTH 981 mm 38.64 in
BARREL LENGTH 607 mm 23.9 in
WEIGHT W/O WATER 14.7 kg 32.6 lb
WEIGHT OF TRIPOD 23.9 kg 53.15 lb
WEIGHT COMPLETE W/O WATER 38.5 kg
    85.75 lb
M.V. 854 m/s 2800 ft/sec
RATE OF FIRE 450-600 rpm
TYPE OF FEED 250 fabric or metal link
    belt

Despite the fact that the Browning M1917 machine gun went into service in 1917 the gun actually started its development as far back as the late 1890s and was held up mainly by lack of interest by the military authorities. Unlike the earlier Browning designs, the M1917 used a recoil-operated mechanism which, once finalised, remained virtually unchanged in all future Browning designs, The M1917 was a water-cooled gun that resembled in appearance the British Vickers gun, but it had a pistol grip instead of the British double spade grip. The M1917 was turned out in thousands by a variety of manufacturers and was gradually modified until a drastic revision produced the M1917A1 in 1936. The M1917A1 was outwardly the same as the earlier version, but there were changes to the feed, sights and tripod mounting.

1, 2, 3. M1917A1 5. M1917 in action near Naples 1943 4, 6. The Polish Browning Model 30 which was referred to by the Germans as either the 7.9 mm sMG 249(p) or MG 30(p)

1

The revised version became the standard support machine gun of the US Army during WW2 and served on for many years after. In 1974 it still serves on with many armies. In 1939 some Browning machine guns were in use by Poland as the Ciezki karabin maszynowy wz.30. After the defeat of Poland these guns fell into German and Russian hands. The German designation became 7.9 mm sMG 249(p) and the Russian guns retained their Polish designation in its shortened form as CKM wz.30, and do not appear to have been widely used by them. Some M1917 guns were also issued to the Russians under Lease-lend, and others were used in China in 7.92 mm calibre. The Belgian FN plant produced many M1917 guns for export prior to 1939, mainly to South American states. During WW2 53,854 M1917 A1 guns were produced as opposed to the total of 68,389 M1917 models previous to that. In 1940, 10,000 M1917 guns were sold to the UK and used for home defence.

2

3

4

5

6

US Machine Gun, Caliber .30″, M1919

DATA
M1919A4/M1919A6
CALIBRE 7.62 mm 0.30 in
    7.62 mm 0.30 in
LENGTH 1041 mm 41 in
    1346 mm 53 in
BARREL LENGTH 610 mm 24 in
    610 mm 24 in
WEIGHT 13.95 kg 31 lb
    14.6 kg 32.5 lb
M.V. 854 m/s 2800 ft/sec
RATE OF FIRE 400-500 rpm
TYPE OF FEED 250 round fabric or metal
    link belt

The Browning M1919 differed from the M1917 only in using an air-cooled barrel, as it employed the same basic mechanism. The first version, the M1919, was intended as a tank gun but the tanks it was intended for were never built and it was further developed into the M1919A1, M1919A2 (intended for use with cavalry) and the M1919A3. None of these guns were produced in quantity. The M1919A4 was intended for use either as a fixed AFV gun or for flexible mountings. It rapidly became one of the most widely used machine guns of WW2. During WW2 438,971 were produced and the M1919A4 is still in use all over the world. It was issued to just about all the Allied combatants in WW2 who found it a most satisfactory and reliable weapon. Nearly all the M1919A4 guns produced were infantry weapons as the M1919A5 was found to be more satisfactory for AFV use. The M1919A6 was produced as an infantry squad weapon by adding a bipod, butt and carrying handle to the M1919A4. It soon became a very popular and useful infantry machine gun despite the fact that it is still rather heavy for a light machine gun. One oddity about the M1919A6 is that despite its widespread use it has always been regarded as a 'substitute' standard gun as far as the US forces are concerned. During its life there have been numerous changes and modifications to the M1919A4 and A6 series but they still remain two of the most reliable and efficient of all machine guns produced. A total of 43,479 M1919A6 guns were manufactured. The M1919 was also used as the basis for a range of aircraft machine guns (the M2) and also as the basis of the US Navy aircraft gun, the AN-M2.

1

2

3

4

1, 2, 4. M1919A4   3. These Canadians in Italy in May 1944 have added a rough carrying handle to their M1919A4 5. M1919A6

5

The Browning .50" Machine Guns

The first .50 in Browning machine gun was produced in 1921 as the M1921, and it was basically an enlarged version of the .30 in M1917 mechanism firing a .50 in round based on the German 13 mm round used in the German T-Gewehr anti-tank rifle. This gun was developed into the M2 which then formed the basis of a series of heavy machine guns all using the same mechanism and differing only in the method of installation and the type of barrel used. One of the first variants was the M2 water-cooled gun which was used as an anti-aircraft gun and was installed on many US Navy vessels. Another version was the M2HB which was an air-cooled version with a heavy barrel (HB) for use in fixed installations, as an AFV turret weapon and also as an aircraft turret gun. There was a basic version of the M2 which had a lighter barrel that could not be used for sustained fire and another that was intended as a fixed installation aircraft gun. The M2 versions were produced in large numbers (over 1,485,000 of the aircraft version were made) and in fact, more .50 in guns have been made than any other American machine gun. It was, and still is, a very reliable machine gun with devastating fire power. One facet of its detail design is that any part of any M2 and M1921 gun can be inter-changed with any other M2 gun with the exception of the barrel which was 36 in for aircraft guns and 45 in for ground guns. In 1944 an increased rate of fire version of the aircraft gun was introduced as the M3, and this also used a 36 in barrel. Many aircraft guns were used on ground and ship mountings. The Japanese produced a direct copy of the M2 as the 12.7 mm Type 1.

DATA (M2HB Flexible)
CALIBRE   12.7 mm   0.50 in
LENGTH   1654 mm   65.1 in
BARREL LENGTH   1143 mm   45 in
WEIGHT   37.8 kg   84 lb
M.V.   884 m/s   2900 ft/sec
RATE OF FIRE   450-575 rpm
TYPE OF FEED   110 round metal link belt

1. .50 in M2   2. M2 in the Marshall Islands
3. M2 on M63 AA mounting   4. M2HB
5. M2   6. M2 nest in Germany, 1945, with spare barrel ready for use   7, 8, 9. Water-cooled M2

1

2

3

4

5

6

7

8

9

Colt-Browning Export Models

Between the wars the American Colt company produced commercial versions of the Browning M1917 and 1917A1 for export. They were known as the MG38 and MG38B, and the main difference between the two was that the MG38B had spade grips instead of the pistol grip of the MG38 and M1917, but they were otherwise different from the military model in detail only. They were sold widely, and Norway was one of the few European customers for the MG38B. Their guns were in 7.9 mm calibre and there were two versions. One was used by the Norwegians as the Colt mitraljose m/29 I, and another as the Colt mitraljose m/29 T. In 1940 the Germans took them over for occupation duties as the 7.9 mm sMG 245/1 and 245/2(n). A few 7.92 mm calibre models were sold to China, and large numbers went to other Asiatic and South American states. There was an air-cooled version of the MG38 known as the MG40 and Norway also used a few of these as the Colt mitraljose m/29, mainly as aircraft weapons.

DATA (MG38B)
CALIBRE 7.9 mm 0.311 in
LENGTH 1110 mm 43.7 in
BARREL LENGTH 607 mm 23.9 in
WEIGHT WITH WATER 18.5 kg 40.8 lb
M.V. 854 m/s 2800 ft/sec
RATE OF FIRE 500 rpm
TYPE OF FEED 250 round belt

Colt-Browning Model MG38B

The Johnson Light Machine Gun Model 1941

The Johnson Light Machine Gun was derived from the earlier Johnson Automatic Rifle, and was a very light weapon with many unusual features. It had a variable fire-rate, used a recoil-operated mechanism that fired from a closed bolt for single shots and an open bolt for automatic. It was ordered by the Dutch government for use in the Dutch East Indies but it was never delivered and some were issued to the US Marines and Special Service units. It soon proved to be underdeveloped and troublesome, so large orders were not made. Accounts exist of the US Marines throwing them away in action and using other guns. Production of US machine guns was concentrated on existing models, so despite further development of the Johnson into the unsuccessful Model 1944, it was never widely used. For all its faults in action, the Johnson had many novel features that were later incorporated into later machine gun designs. After the war the Israelis built the Model 1944 as the Dror machine gun, but only in small numbers.

DATA
CALIBRE 7.62 mm 0.30 in
LENGTH 1067 mm 42 in
BARREL LENGTH 559 mm 22 in
WEIGHT 6.45 kg 14.3 lb
M.V. 853 m/s 2800 ft/sec
RATE OF FIRE Variable 300-900 rpm
TYPE OF FEED 20 round box magazine

Johnson Light Machine Gun

USSR

Pulemet Maksima Obrazets 1910

DATA
CALIBRE 7.62 mm 0.30 in
LENGTH 1107 mm 43.6 in
BARREL LENGTH 720 mm 28.4 in
WEIGHT OF GUN 23.8 kg 52.5 lb
WEIGHT OF MOUNT WITH SHIELD 45.2 kg
 99.71 lb
WEIGHT COMPLETE 74.0 kg 152.5 lb
M.V. 863 m/s 2822 ft/sec
RATE OF FIRE 520-600 rpm
TYPE OF FEED 250 round fabric belt

Of all the many variants that have been produced from the basic Maxim machine gun, the award for the version with the longest life and heaviest construction must go to the Russian series that began with the Pulemet Maksima obr. 1910. This gun faithfully copied the Maxim mechanism unchanged, and it was first produced in 1905 as the PM1905 with a bronze water jacket. In 1910 this was changed to the PM1910 which differed only in having a steel water jacket, and it was this version that was produced in vast numbers until about 1943 virtually unchanged. The gun was very heavily built and could take a lot of rough handling, which it often had to, but above all it was reliable. It could carry on firing under a wide range of conditions and in all climates, and it remains in service with some Soviet Satellite states in 1974. During its production life the PM1910 underwent some minor changes, typical of which was a filler cap on top of the water jacket which was fashioned from a tractor radiator cap, but the basic mechanism was unchanged. The gun was mounted on a wide variety of possible mounts of which the Sokolov carriage was the most common. This was virtually a small artillery carriage with steel wheels, a traversing turntable and a U-shaped hand-towing trail. Some Sokolov mountings had a small shield as well but this was often left off as the mounting was quite heavy enough already. For AA work the PM1910 could be mounted on a special AA tripod but there were also trucks equipped to carry special quadruple-mounted installations, some of which were mounted statically as the Model 1931 mounting. The Tachanka was the name given to a horse-drawn cart mounting two PM1910s for AA work—Sokolov mountings, wheels and all. There were many other specialized mountings produced as well as a host of field lash-ups, all of them with one thing in common—weight. The PM1910 continued in widescale service throughout WW2 despite the introduction of the SG43, and was issued to many friendly states as the war continued. Not surprisingly, the Germans were happy to use the PM1910 as the 7.62 mm sMG 216(r), but they didn't like the idea of dragging it about and used it mainly in static defences.

1. *M1910* **2.** *First type of M1910* **3.** *Final model of M1910 with tractor-type filler cap*

4, 5, 6. M1910 on Sokolov mounting
7, 8. M1910 equipped with AA sights and
mounting   9. Quad mounting of the M1910
on a sledge   10. A M1910 mounted on a
tachanka

4

5

6

7

8

9

10

Pulemet Degtyareva Pekhotnii (DP)

DATA

CALIBRE 7.62 mm 0.30 in
LENGTH 1265 mm 49.8 in
BARREL LENGTH 605 mm 23.8 in
WEIGHT 11.9 kg 26.23 lb
M.V. 844 m/s 2770 ft/sec
RATE OF FIRE 520-580 rpm
TYPE OF FEED 47 round drum

The DP light machine gun has a place in history as being the first truly Russian machine gun to see service. It was designed during the early 1920s by Vasily Alexeyevich Degtyarev, and the first model was submitted in 1926 as the DP1926, and field tested against two modified light Maxim guns. In 1928, this gun, with a few modifications, was taken into Russian service as the DP1928, or as it is usually known, the DP. Ever since 1928 the DP has been one of the finest guns in its class, for it is simple, light, robust and reliable. The simple gas-operated mechanism has only six moving parts and the system can operate well under a wide range of conditions. The DP was used in very large numbers throughout WW2 and remains in service with many states in 1974. The main weakness of the DP was the operating spring under the barrel which became hot during prolonged firing and this caused the spring to grow weak with resultant malfunctions. This shortcoming was modified out with the 1944 DPM. There was an aircraft gun variant known as the DA and a tank version, the DT. German designation was 7.62 mm leMG 120(r).

1, 2, 4, 6, 7. DP1928   3. DP1928 with bipod secured for steadiness   5. DP1928 at Stalingrad   8. DP1928 behind an armoured shield

1

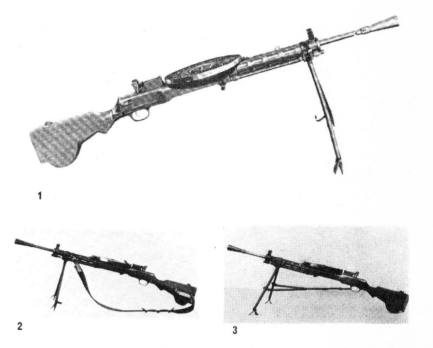

2

3

4

5

6

7

8

DP1928

Pulemet Degtyareva Tankovii (DT)

The DT was a close relative of the DP and was first issued in 1929. It was designed for use in armoured vehicles, but was mechanically the same as the DP. It used an adjustable metal butt and could be fitted with a bipod for ground use. The DT was fitted to most of the Russian tanks used during WW2 including the famous T34 series. For tank use the barrel was heavier than that of the DP and the magazine was different.

DATA

CALIBRE	7.62 mm	0.30 in
LENGTH	1181 mm	46.5 in
BARREL LENGTH	597 mm	23.5 in

WEIGHT	12.69 kg	27.91 lb
M.V.	839 m/s	2756 ft/sec
RATE OF FIRE	600 rpm	
TYPE OF FEED	60 round drum	

1

1. DT tank gun   2. DT gun dismounted for infantry use   3. A DT gun on an improvised AA mount   4. DT gun in action near Leningrad   5. DT tank gun on roof mounting

2

3

4

5

Degtyarev Aircraft Machine Guns

Another version of the basic Degtyarev DP gun was a series of guns intended for use in aircraft. There was one basic type with a few minor variants, but most seem to have been covered by the DA designation. First produced in 1931, by 1941 they had been replaced by later models in aircraft and were issued to ground forces as stop-gap AA weapons. They were easily recognizable by the prominent muzzle attachment.

DATA

CALIBRE	7.62 mm	0.30 in
LENGTH	995 mm	39.2 in
BARREL LENGTH	605 mm	23.8 in

WEIGHT	7.2 kg	15.8 lb
M.V.	844 m/s	2770 ft/sec
RATE OF FIRE	550 rpm	
TYPE OF FEED	60 round drum	

Degtyarov Aircraft gun

Pulemet Degtyareva Pekhotnii Modificatsionii 1944

DATA
CALIBRE   7.62 mm   0.30 in
LENGTH   1265 mm   49. 8in
BARREL LENGTH   605 mm   23.8 in
WEIGHT   12.2 kg   26.8 lb
M.V.   844 m/s   2770 ft/sec
RATE OF FIRE   520-580 rpm
TYPE OF FEED   47 round drum

The DP1928 did have some faults that affected its performance in action, one of which was the operating spring under the barrel that grew weak when heated by the barrel after prolonged firing. This weak spring caused troubles and in 1944 the DPM1944, or DPM, was produced with the spring fitted at the rear of the bolt. In this position it protruded over the butt in a small housing which prevented the firer gripping the small of the butt so a pistol grip had to be fitted. Another change was to the bipod which was revised and strengthened, and the grip safety was removed. The DPM was a great success with the front-line troops and it remains in widespread service to this day. The DTM was exactly the same gun as the earlier DT, but with the operating spring modification added.

DPM1944

DTM

The ShKAS Aircraft Guns

DATA
CALIBRE   7.62 mm   0.30 in
LENGTH   960 mm   37.8 in
BARREL LENGTH   605 mm   23.8 in
WEIGHT   10.5 kg   23.2 lb
M.V.   740 m/s   2430 ft/sec
RATE OF FIRE   1800-2000 rpm
TYPE OF FEED   Belt

There were three models of the ShKAS machine gun—the KM33, 35, 36 and 41. They were all aircraft cockpit machine guns, although they could be used in a fixed mounting, and thus had a high rate of fire. The KM33 was never produced in large numbers but the main production models, the KM35 and KM36, were turned out in thousands. These two models were almost identical and during World War 2 were often used on ground mountings as anti-aircraft guns. They were rather complicated gas-operated guns that had an unusual ejector system that ejected spent cases forward, but they were reliable and robust and remained in use for many years after the war—some were encountered in Korea. Although it used the standard Russian calibre of 7.62 mm, the ShKAS series used a special cartridge.

1. A much-modified ShKAS gun covering a river crossing near Stalingrad, November 1942.
2. ShKAS KM36

1

2

Krasnoi Pulemet Degtyereva-Shpagina Obrazets 1938G

In 1938 the heavy 12.7 mm DShK1938 entered service with the Russian Army and in 1974 it still remains in service with them. Intended as a heavy support weapon its nearest Western equivalent is the .50 in Browning, but unlike that recoil-operated gun it uses the Degtyarev gas-operated system allied to a feed system designed by Georgiy Shpagin. It was a very successful weapon that was eventually used for a variety of roles, among them being the secondary armament for armoured vehicles including the well-known heavy IS-3 tanks. For ground use the mounting already produced for the PM1910 Maxim gun was used, modified to produce the Model 1938 mounting, and a special AA mounting was produced. The DShK1938 was also mounted on small coastal craft and armoured trains. For AA use there were twin and quadruple mountings which operated in cooperation with searchlights.

DATA

CALIBRE   12.7 mm   0.50 in
LENGTH   1602 mm   62.3 in
BARREL LENGTH   1002 mm   39.4 in
WEIGHT   33.3 kg   73.5 lb
M.V.   843 m/s   2765 ft/sec
RATE OF FIRE   550-600 rpm
TYPE OF FEED   50 round metal link belt, joined to provide 250 rounds

DshK1938

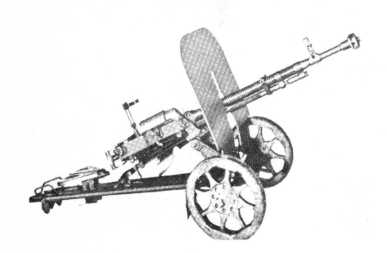

Pulemet Obrazets 1939

A pre-war attempt to produce a Maxim replacement was a Degtyarev design, the DS1939. It was a scaled-down version of the heavy DShK1938, and despite its apparently simple mechanism there were many operating difficulties, and the gun was difficult to produce. Production and introduction into service began in 1939 but by 1942 Russian production facilities were being stretched by the huge German advances and at such a time an expensive and troublesome weapon such as the DS1939 could not survive and production ceased. By 1943 all serving DS1939 guns had been withdrawn. The DS1939 was air-cooled and gas-operated and could fire at two rates—550 rpm for ground use and 1100 rpm for AA use. The rate could be changed by altering the gas regulator and changing the buffer spring tension, but it was this feature that gave most of the trouble which led to the demise of the gun.

DATA
CALIBRE 7.62 mm   0.30 in
LENGTH 1171 mm   46.1 in
BARREL LENGTH 721 mm   28.4 in
WEIGHT OF GUN 12 kg   26.4 lb
M.V. 863 m/s   2830 ft/sec
RATE OF FIRE 520-580 or 1020-1180 rpm
TYPE OF FEED 50 round metal link belt

1 to 4. DS1939   5. DS1939 in 1942. The rifleman is using a Simonov automatic rifle

1

2

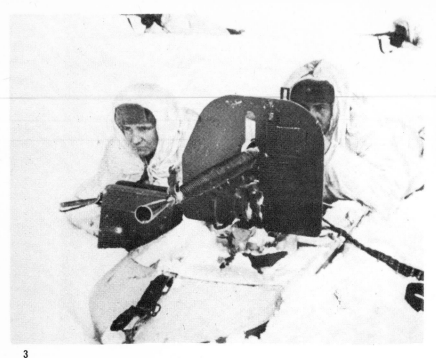

DS1939
DS1939 in 1942. The rifleman is using a Simonov automatic rifle

4

5

Stankovii Pulemet Goryunova Obrazets 1943G

During the early 1940s it was realized that the elderly PM1910 machine guns were being surpassed in performance by lighter and more modern guns so the Goryunov brothers designed the gun that was to be known as the SG1943, or SG43. They produced a gas-operated air-cooled gun that was so successful that in 1974 it is only just going out of service with the Russian forces, and is still in front line use elsewhere. The mechanism is a combination of Degtyarev, Browning and a few other principles used in such a way that the principle can be termed original, and the system is very robust and can operate under a wide range of conditions. The SG43 has undergone many modifications but most of them are post-war. One variant is the SGMT tank gun usually used in a co-axial mounting, and the SGMB which was a special version for mounting on vehicles. Although it was intended as a PM1910 replacement the SG43 did not replace the old Maxim gun before 1945, and not even for many years after that.

SG43

DATA
CALIBRE	7.62 mm	0.30 in
LENGTH	1120 mm	44.1 in
BARREL LENGTH	719 mm	28.3 in
WEIGHT	13.8 kg	30.4 lb

WEIGHT OF MOUNT	26.9 kg	59.3 lb
WEIGHT COMPLETE	40.7 kg	89.7 lb
M.V.	863 m/s	2830 ft/sec
RATE OF FIRE	500-640 rpm	
TYPE OF FEED	50 round metal link belt	

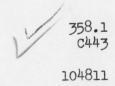